ABIOGENESIS

INTRODUCING MODERN SCIENCE

ABIOGENESIS

From Molecules to Cells

PAUL D. THOMPSON

Helen Hale, Editorial Consultant

Illustrations by Mary Lybarger

J. B. Lippincott Company

PHILADELPHIA NEW YORK

Printed in the United States of America
Library of Congress Catalog Card Number 78-82399
FIRST EDITION
Typography by Tere LoPrete

To My Parents

ACKNOWLEDGMENTS

THE AUTHOR IS grateful for the help of many individuals in the preparation of this book. Particular thanks should go to the following persons who took time to read portions of the manuscript related to their specialties, and offered their valuable criticisms and suggestions: Dr. Aaron Ihde, of the University of Wisconsin Chemistry Department; Dr. Lowell Noland, emeritus professor of zoology at the University of Wisconsin; Dr. David Clark, of the University of Wisconsin Geology Department; and Mr. Robert McCauley, of the Institute of Molecular Evolution at the University of Miami in Florida. The author, however, must accept full responsibility for any errors of fact or interpretation.

The following persons and organizations are thanked for contributing illustrations: Dr. John Cairns, Cold Spring Harbor Laboratory of Quantitative Biology—Figure 5–3; Dr. Paul

Hoffman—Figures 7–2 and 7–3; Dr. Elso Barghoorn—Figures 7–4, 7–5, and 7–6; Institute of Molecular Evolution, University of Miami—Figures 10–1 and 10–2; U.S. Geological Survey—Figure 8–2; National Aeronautics and Space Administration—Figures 9–3 and 13–2; Mt. Wilson and Palomar Observatories—Figures 13–1 and 13–3. The drawing in Figure 13–4 was adapted from a NASA illustration, and the drawings in Figures 2–1 and 2–4 were adapted from illustrations of the United States Department of Agriculture.

CONTENTS

ABIOGENESIS

1

THE ELEMENTS OF LIFE

There is hardly a part of our planet's surface that does not have its quota of plants and animals. The very soil teems with earthworms, insects, and fungi. Scientists find microbes entombed in Antarctic ice and filaments of algae growing in the steaming hot springs of Yellowstone. Not only is life widespread, it is incredibly rich in variety. Biologists have discovered and classified more than a million distinct species of plants and animals, and more are being found each day. These species are interrelated in often subtle and complex ways. The hawk eats rabbits and other small animals. Rabbits feed on such plants as the pea vines in the vegetable garden. The peas, in their turn, need certain bacteria inhabiting nodules on their roots to convert atmospheric nitrogen to compounds which the plants can use.

The fossil record in the rocks shows us that the tapestry of life has not always had the same pattern. Some species die out, while new ones arise as offshoots of older kinds of organisms. New relationships evolve between plants, animals, and their environment. Also, the geological record shows that life has not always had its present range and complexity. Going back in time we find that millions of years ago life was restricted to the creatures of the seas, and the land and the air were barren. Back still farther, life existed only in the form of simple plants and animals of only one or a few cells. It is believed that in the very early years of Earth's history there was no life. Our planet was a dead sphere, a sterile bit of celestial dust.

What conditions on our planet made it suitable for the genesis of life, and its luxuriant later development? for abiogenesis, the generation of living organisms from nonliving matter?

One very essential condition was probably the presence of liquid water. Water is the most plentiful substance found in living things; nearly two thirds of our bodies are water. It performs a multitude of functions in organisms, one of the most important of which is acting as a solvent. A tremendous number of substances dissolve in water. The food our cells need reaches them dissolved in the blood stream, and the blood also carries away dissolved waste products. The cell itself is mostly water, and many of the other materials of the cell are dissolved or suspended in the water.

The fact that liquid water exists on our planet is due to our globe's location in relation to the sun. It lies in what has been called the temperate zone of the solar system: if its orbit were as close to the sun as Mercury's, its surface would be so hot that all water would boil away; on the other hand, if the Earth were much more distant from the sun than it is, our water would be permanently frozen.

Another vital consideration in the genesis of life must have been the presence of an atmosphere. Our atmosphere provides the gases that animals and plants need for respiration and photosynthesis. In addition, it transports the water vapor needed for the rains and snows that make the ocean's moisture available to the continents. The air also acts as a shield against deadly cosmic radiation, much of it from the sun. The sun is constantly pouring out X rays, ultraviolet radiation, and other rays. Without the blanket of the atmosphere, more of these radiations would reach Earth's surface, and might make life impossible, at least on the exposed land masses.

So far we have been speaking as if everyone knew just what life is, and how it differs from nonlife. To a certain extent, everybody *does* know what life is. One way we identify living things is by their movement: the gull skims over the surface of the ocean; the sunflower turns its head to follow the sun; the squirrel runs up the tree trunk. Life is also growth—baby into man, seed into elm. Then too, all living forms reproduce their own kind, whether it be a bacterium's splitting in two or Mrs. Jones down the block coming home from the hospital with a new baby. In addition, living things respond to their environment. The root tip grows toward the source of moisture. The citizen writes a letter to the newspaper complaining about the increase in property taxes.

A crystal in a chemical solution can grow, the flame of a

match can reproduce itself and cause a forest fire, and an avalanche can move with frightening rapidity. Yet we do not call these things living creatures. For a thing usually must have more than just one of the characteristics of life before we call it living. There are borderline cases. The kind of microorganism called a virus does not grow or move under its own power. When it comes into contact with a cell, however, it does respond by penetrating the cell, and once inside it reproduces. For these reasons many biologists consider viruses to be living organisms, though some would not.

The virus illustrates a major problem in defining life. Nonlife seems to shade imperceptibly into life. It seems as impossible to draw a sharp boundary between the two as it is to point out the exact instant when a boy becomes a man. (Modern medicine faces a somewhat comparable problem of defining the difference between life and death. Is a person dead when his heart stops beating? When his brain stops functioning? Or when the last cell of the body dies, many hours after heartbeat stops?)

Once we identify a creature as being alive, we may well wonder what makes it alive—how does it get its ability to grow, move, respond? One answer might be to assume that there is a spark or "breath of life" that resides in organisms and gives them their vitality. This theory used to be very popular among a number of people, including many biologists. The concept fitted in very well with religious ideas on the origin of life. The Bible portrays God creating life from inanimate matter. One could visualize the Creator infusing the vital spirit into inert dust, a spirit that was passed on from generation to generation of living creatures as they obeyed the divine command to "be fruitful and multiply."

However, starting several centuries ago, scientists began to explain many of the functions of living things in physical and chemical terms. The human arm was observed to be a set of levers that operated according to well-known laws of physics. Respiration, the production of energy from food in the presence of oxygen, was explained as a kind of burning very like the combustion in a candle flame.

Gradually, a school of thought arose that held that *all* the functions of life would eventually be understandable in physical and chemical terms. Just as the "vital spark" theory lent itself to a religious interpretation of the creation of life, so the newer theory suggests a materialistic explanation—life must have arisen from the right combination of atoms and molecules. This concept is not necessarily incompatible with religion.

Going on the assumption that life is basically physical and chemical in nature, scientists have made many remarkable discoveries and have greatly increased our understanding of living things. However, the idea that all the phenomena of life, including consciousness and thought, can be explained in physical and chemical terms remains an assumption, not a proven fact.

The subject of this book is the origin of life, or abiogenesis. Before we can discuss in detail what scientists are learning about life's beginnings, it is necessary to learn some of the important things that researchers have discovered about present-day living things. We must consider such questions as: How are living things organized? What substances are found in them? What are some of the important chemical reactions that keep life going? These questions will be taken up in the first few chapters of the book. The later chapters are devoted to the history of life on Earth, and what scientists are discovering about the origin of life.

Before the invention of the microscope, early anatomists had discovered that organisms such as man are made up of a number of parts that work together. These parts, or organs, are composed of various kinds of material, or tissue. Each tissue has its own characteristic structure and "feel." Muscle tissue is firm and fibrous; fatty tissue is yielding and blubbery.

Early microscopists discovered boxlike structures, or cells, in plant and animal tissues. In 1838, the German scientist Mathias Schleiden announced a theory that the cell was the basic building-block of all plants. The next year, the cell theory was broadened by another German scientist, Theodore Schwann, to include animals. Thus, living organisms were seen as communities of cells working together cooperatively to perform the various functions of the body. The cell theory proved to be one of the great generalizations of science. Aside from viruses, which are generally considered to be below the cell on the scale of life, most biologists today hold that all organisms are made up of one or more cells and their products.

Living cells are filled with a transparent, jelly-like substance called protoplasm. In 1861, the German researcher Max Schultze established the generalization that animal and plant protoplasm are essentially alike. Since living things are made up of cells, and all cells are largely protoplasm, we cannot go too far wrong if we assume that one important key to the understanding of life lies in studying protoplasm and its activities. This has been the main thrust of modern biochemistry, the chemistry of life.

One way to examine protoplasm is to analyze it chemically. When the human body is chemically analyzed, we find the following composition by weight:

		Per cent
MAJOR ELEMENTS	Oxygen	65
	Carbon	18
	Hydrogen	10
	Nitrogen	3
	Calcium	2
	Phosphorus	1
SECONDARY ELEMENTS	Potassium	0.35
	Sulfur	0.25
	Chlorine	0.15
	Sodium	0.15
	Magnesium	0.05
	Iron	0.004
	Other Elements	0.046

The atoms of these elements come together in various combinations to form molecules of chemical compounds. At this point, it will be useful to review our knowledge of atoms and how they combine into molecules. An atom is a very tiny particle of matter too small to be viewed directly under any microscope. In our universe, we find some 100-odd basic kinds of atoms; a few of these have not been discovered in nature but have been created in the laboratory. A substance made up of one kind of atom is an element.

Some atoms are chemical "loners" and seldom or never join together with other atoms. Most atoms, however, have the ability to form various combinations with other atoms. Such a grouping of atoms is called a molecule. The oxygen of the air, for example, is a gas made up of molecules. Each molecule is a pair of oxygen atoms. This molecule can be represented in chemical shorthand by the letter that stands for the element, plus a small subscript number to indicate that there are two atoms of oxygen in the molecule: O_2. The elements hydrogen and nitrogen also are usually composed of molecules, that can be represented as H_2 and N_2.

Atoms have the power to combine not only with other atoms of the same kind but with atoms of different elements. If we place a pure, untarnished piece of iron in a container of oxygen, the surface of the iron eventually becomes covered with a film of rust. This rusting is the result of union between iron atoms and oxygen atoms to form molecules of iron oxide.

Substances whose molecules contain more than one element are called compounds. Living things are composed of a number of elements, most of them in the form of compounds. The study of the chemical compounds found in living things, and the processes by which they are formed and destroyed, is known as biochemistry.

The atom contains smaller particles, such as electrons, that are responsible for its chemical behavior. (See Appendix A for a fuller discussion of how the structure of the atom affects its chemical activity, and how various chemical bonds are formed.) Some of these particles carry positive electrical charges, while certain others have negative electrical charges. Ordinarily, these charges balance each other and cancel out, so the atom is electrically neutral. Most stable molecules are electrically neutral, also. However, it is possible for an atom or a molecule to become electrically unbalanced, so that it carries an overall positive or negative charge. Such a charged atom or molecule is called an ion. Ions perform important jobs in the living organism.

About 65 per cent of the human body is water. The water molecule is made up of two hydrogen atoms linked to an oxygen atom and is symbolized as H_2O.

The molecules of water in protoplasm are, of course, separated by empty space. In addition, they are in constant motion, hurtling about like so many tennis balls, colliding and changing course. A molecule moves forward until its progress is deflected by a collision with another molecule; its path resembles a "drunkard's walk," two steps in one direction, three steps in another, and then perhaps a step backward.

The molecules in a liquid do not move completely independently of each other, as they would if more widely separated in a gas. There are certain forces of attraction between them so that it is difficult for a single molecule to escape from the group. That is why water poured into a pan remains there and does not immediately disappear into the air. (Of course, the water will eventually evaporate as individual molecules manage to escape into the air one by one.)

One force of attraction between water molecules results from the fact that the electrical charges in the H_2O molecule are not evenly distributed. As shown in Figure 1–1, the oxygen atom is located between two hydrogen atoms. Because the electrical charges of the molecule are unevenly distributed, the part of the molecule in the neighborhood of the oxygen atom carries a strong negative charge, while the two hydrogen atoms each bear a somewhat weaker positive charge.

The water molecule can be visualized as a bar with its ends oppositely charged. Scientists call such a structure an electrical dipole. We know that unlike electrical charges attract.

1–1 *The dipolar water molecule.*

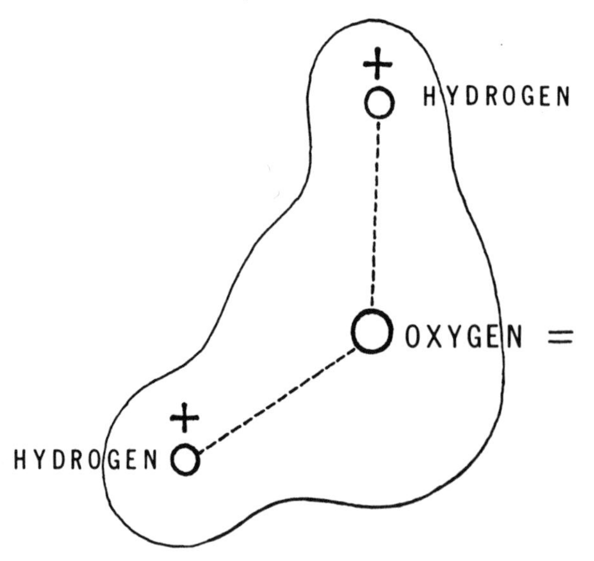

When two water molecules are near each other, the positive charge of one dipole tends to attract the negative charge of the other. If the two molecules are moving very slowly, or are following a roughly parallel course, they may cling to each other. We can visualize many of the molecules of the water being held together by a network of "polar bonds," as these forces of attraction are called. However, the polar bond is comparatively weak, and the molecules in their motion are constantly breaking and reforming bonds.

Although the water molecule is a dipole, its overall electrical charge is neutral. In protoplasm, however, we find dissolved atoms and molecules that are not electrically neutral but carry an overall positive or negative charge. Ordinary table salt, sodium chloride, is a compound made up of sodium and chlorine atoms in equal numbers. When dissolved in water, the individual atoms separate. The sodium atoms carry a positive charge, while the chlorine atoms are negative ions. These ions are found in large numbers in protoplasm and in the body fluids. Other elements are present, too, in ionic form. Ions are usually identified with plus or minus signs placed next to their chemical symbols.

Among the more important single-atom ions in the body are sodium (Na^{+}), chlorine (Cl^{-}), calcium (Ca^{++}), potassium (K^{+}), and magnesium (Mg^{--}). In addition, there are multiatomic ions formed when certain compounds are dissolved in water. Among the most important are phosphate ions, such as PO_4^{---}. These ions containing phosphorus take part in a number of important chemical reactions in the cell.

From time to time, a water molecule will break up due to a collision. It will divide into two fragments, each of which is an ion. One is the hydrogen ion, H^+, and the other is the hydroxyl ion, OH^-. This breakup is a comparatively rare event; only one out of every 555,555,555 water molecules at any given time is split apart in this fashion.

Chemists have found that the acidity of a watery solution is related to the hydrogen and hydroxyl ions present. The sour substances that we call acids (lemon juice gets its sour taste from the citric acid it contains) contribute hydrogen ions when dissolved in water. An acid solution has more hydrogen ions than hydroxyl ions. The substances known as bases, however, contribute hydroxyl ions and tend to make the solution alkaline. Pure water, because it contains an equal number of hydrogen and hydroxyl ions, is neutral, neither acid nor alkaline. Protoplasm is slightly alkaline, but is very close to neutrality. Certain compounds in protoplasm help to maintain this state by chemically combining with excess hydrogen or hydroxyl ions. These substances, known as "buffers" to the chemist, are very important to life, for without them the cell could easily become too acid or alkaline for its major chemical processes to take place.

Many of the ions found in protoplasm and the body fluids are also found in sea water; this may point to the fact that life arose in the sea and incorporated its elements and compounds.

Perhaps the single most important element in protoplasm is carbon. The element gets its importance from the fact that its atoms are tremendously versatile in forming bonds with other atoms. Carbon has the ability to form an extraordinary number of different molecules, including the large, elaborate molecules that are characteristic of living things. The carbon atom can combine with up to four other atoms. We can represent the atom as having four "arms," or bonds, that it can use to link with other atoms:

```
  |
—C—
  |
```

Carbon atoms can link to each other to form diamond or graphite. Carbon can also combine with other elements, to form methane, for example:

```
   H
   |
H—C—H
   |
   H
```

The carbon atom may form bonds simultaneously with carbon atoms and other types of atoms. Ethane, for instance:

```
   H  H
   |  |
H—C—C—H
   |  |
   H  H
```

In organic molecules, we often find carbon atoms forming

what are called double and triple bonds. In the ethylene molecule, the carbons share a double bond:

```
H—C═C—H
  |  |
  H  H
```

And in acetylene we find a triple bond:

```
H—C≡C—H
```

Carbon atoms can also link together to form ring molecules, as in benzene:

```
       H
       |
       C
     /   \\
H—C       C—H
  ||      |
H—C       C—H
     \   //
       C
       |
       H
```

The compounds consisting solely of carbon and hydrogen are known as the hydrocarbons. Our richest source of hydrocarbon compounds is petroleum, which is believed to have been formed from the bodies of creatures that lived in prehistoric seas. From crude oil, scientists are able to obtain a large number of hydrocarbons, including those compounds making up gasoline. Chemists can also synthesize thousands of hydrocarbon compounds. It is estimated that somewhere in the vicinity of two million carbon compounds are known to chemistry, many of them hydrocarbons. And many more are synthesized each year.

In living creatures, most of the important compounds contain oxygen in addition to carbon and hydrogen, and many also contain nitrogen.

Carbon linkages form the "backbone" of the vital giant molecules that carry on the main functions of protoplasm. Among these molecules are the proteins, the sugars and starches (carbohydrates), and the fats. These molecules are considerably larger than the water molecules among which they are suspended; the water molecule has a molecular

1–2 *An artist's conception of some of the types of molecules making up protoplasm. The molecules are not drawn to exact scale, and the symbols only suggest the true shapes of the molecules.*

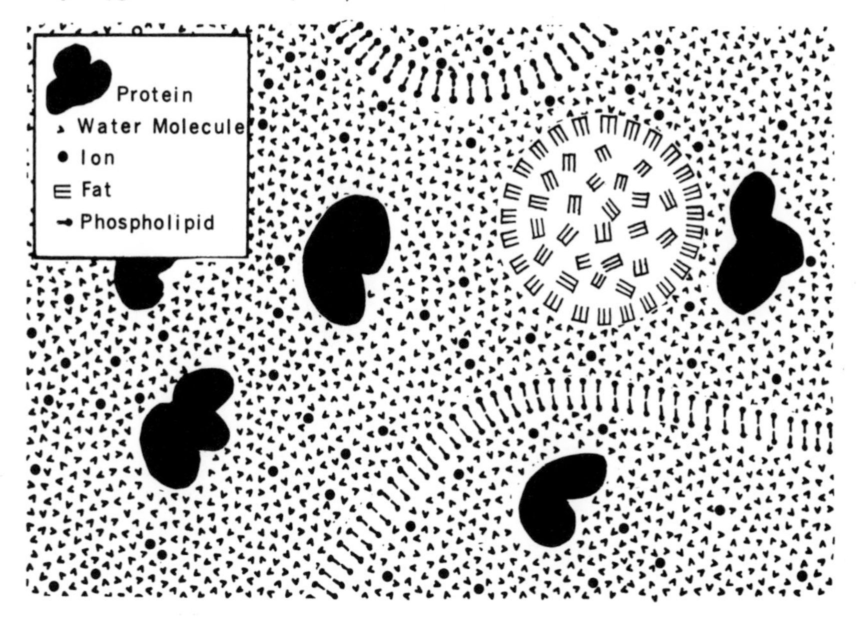

weight of about 18 atomic mass units, while the average carbohydrate molecule weighs around 150 units and the average fatty molecule around 750 units. Protein molecules range in mass from about 20,000 amu to 1,000,000 units. The large molecules resemble giant Gullivers among a crowd of Lilliputian water molecules. Figure 1–2 gives a schematic view of the various kinds of molecules we find in protoplasm.

Bacteria have been among the most closely studied types of cells. In an *Escherichia coli* bacterium, for every protein molecule we can expect to find roughly 25 fat molecules, 200 carbohydrate molecules, 250 ions of the kinds we have discussed, and some 40,000 water molecules.

2

THE MOLECULES OF LIFE

A CENTURY AND A HALF of hard, patient scientific research were needed to lay the foundation for present-day speculations about the origin of life. One of the first jobs to be done was to isolate in pure form the substances found in protoplasm, and to discover their chemical composition.

Since prehistoric times, man has enjoyed the sweetness of certain plant and animal products such as cane sugar and honey. In the early nineteenth century, when France was a world leader in the new science of chemistry, French researchers studied these sweet substances and found that they were all composed of just three elements—carbon, hydrogen, and oxygen. This class of substances came to be called the carbohydrates. It was found that a number of other plant and animal compounds were carbohydrates, including the starch grains found in plant cells, the cellulose forming the woody walls of the cells, and glycogen, a form of starch found in animal cells.

In 1811, an apothecary in St. Petersburg, Russia, found that when starch was heated with sulfuric acid, the sugar glucose could be extracted from the resulting syrup. In 1819, a French scientist discovered that glucose could also be extracted from the cellulose of old linen rags by treating the cloth with sulfuric acid. Thus, it appeared that glucose could be obtained from both starch and cellulose.

It turned out that glucose molecules served as building blocks in the construction of more elaborate carbohydrate molecules. The glucose molecule is made up of six carbon atoms, twelve hydrogen, and six oxygen, and has the chemical formula $C_6H_{12}O_6$. It has a weight of about 180 atomic mass units.

The atoms in the glucose molecule are not simply clumped together at random. They form a ring structure that can be represented like this:

```
            CH2OH
              |
              C ——— O
            / |       \
      H    /  H        \    H
      |   /             \   |
      C                     C
      |  \                / |
      OH  \  OH     H    /  OH
           \  |     |   /
              C ——— C
              |     |
              H     OH
```

Two glucose molecules can link together to form a more

complex sugar, maltose. (In diagraming ring structures, it is a common practice to omit the letters representing the carbon atoms in the ring. The presence of the carbon atoms is understood.)

More elaborate chains of glucose molecules can be con-

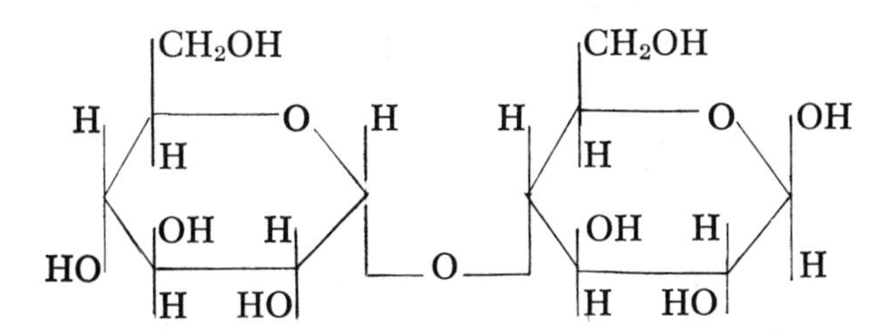

structed, hundreds of units long (Figure 2–1). When glucose

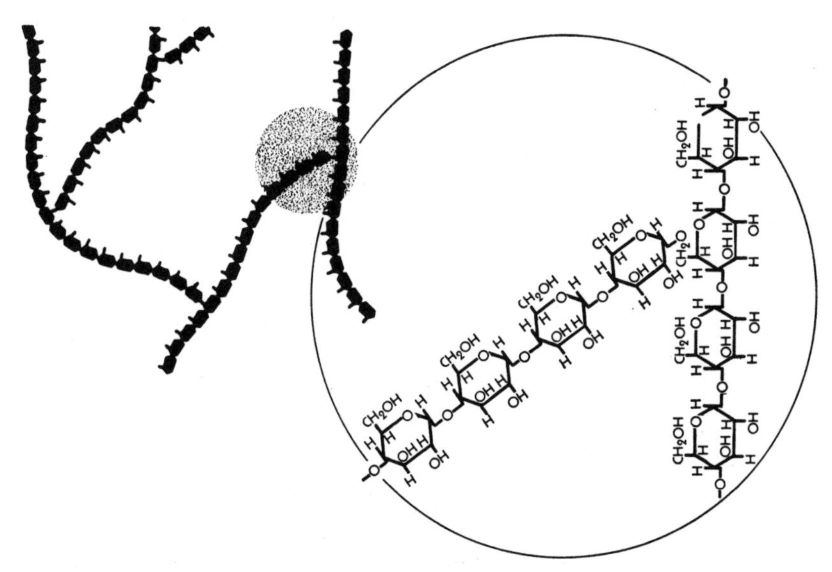

2–1 *Glucose molecules are linked together in chains to form such substances as starch.*

molecules are linked in straight chains of between 300 and 2500 units each, we have cellulose, the important plant structural material that is found in wood, cotton, paper, etc. There is more cellulose in the world than any other organic chemical.

Glucose and similar simple sugars can be dissolved in water, but the more elaborate chains are insoluble. Thus, to store glucose for future use, a plant cell will convert it to starch, which is made up of two kinds of glucose chains—straight ones somewhat similar to shorter cellulose molecules, and elaborate branched chains. Animal cells create branched glucose chains to form glycogen, or animal starch.

In this discussion, we have centered our attention on glucose. There are a number of other simple sugars, such as fructose, that have molecules with ring structures and that can combine to form long chains. However, the basic principle of construction is the same.

The carbohydrates are an example of one of the important basic economies of life. To build a giant molecule in one unit, whole cloth, would require the expenditure of more energy in one step than the cell has available. Instead, the cell constructs the basic building-block molecules one by one, and then links them to form the final molecule. The job of building the giant molecule is thus broken into a series of small steps, each one requiring only a modest expenditure of energy. This construction principle is used not only with the carbohydrates but with the other complex molecules of the cell.

The green plants are the great manufacturers of carbohydrates. Through the process of photosynthesis, the plants build sugars from air and water. The plants use these sugars in structural materials such as cellulose, and also as food substances. In photosynthesis, the energy of sunlight is stored as chemical energy in the bonds between the atoms of sugar molecules. By breaking down the sugars into simpler elements, the plant releases this energy for use in cell processes.

The plant carbohydrates provide the main energy source for the animal kindgom. Through digestion, the plant carbohydrates are broken down into simple sugars which can be used by the animal cell as fuel.

Chemists have discovered other major classes of organic substances besides the carbohydrates, among them the proteins and the fats.

Like carbohydrates, the proteins are found throughout the world of living things, in both the plant and animal kingdoms. Early chemists knew of organic materials, such as white of egg and milk, that coagulated when heated. They termed these albuminous substances. They discovered that nitrogen was one of the elements in albuminous materials. In 1838, the Dutch chemist Gerard Johann Mulder gave the name of *protein* to these nitrogen-containing substances. The name means "first substance," and indeed the proteins are central compounds in the process of life. But the important role of the proteins was not clearly understood until the twentieth century. The proteins are the jacks-of-all-trades in the living organism. Certain protein molecules are enzymes, or organic catalysts, that aid in carrying out the cell's chemical operations. Without the enzymes, the cell could not build up and tear down its organic compounds. Muscle is largely protein, and these compounds also can serve a structural purpose: the hair and fingernails are proteinaceous. This class of compounds also has many other significant roles in both plants and animals.

When broken down chemically, the proteins turn out to be made of subunit molecules called amino acids. The first amino acid to be isolated was cystine, which the chemist Wollaston found in bladder stones in 1810. The first amino acid to be isolated directly from a proteinaceous substance was leucine, which was found in cheese in 1819 and in muscle fiber and wool a year later. Both of these amino acids are made up of carbon, hydrogen, oxygen, and nitrogen.

There are about 20 widely occurring amino acids, and they all share the same general formula, shown in Figure 2–2. The R represents a variety of molecular groups, a different one for each amino acid. These amino acids can be linked together into what is called a peptide chain. The peptide bond is formed from the —COOH group of one amino acid and the $—NH_2$ group of the other, by eliminating two atoms of hydrogen and one of oxygen, i.e., a molecule of water. The part of the amino acid that becomes incorporated into the peptide chain is called an amino acid residue. Short chains are often referred to as peptides; long ones are termed polypeptides. The molecular groups (R) that distinguish the various amino acids project sideways from the main chain and are called "side chains."

Polypeptide chains of hundreds and even thousands of amino acid residues are common. These are truly giant molecules, having molecular weights of thousands of atomic mass units. For example, human insulin has a molecular weight of

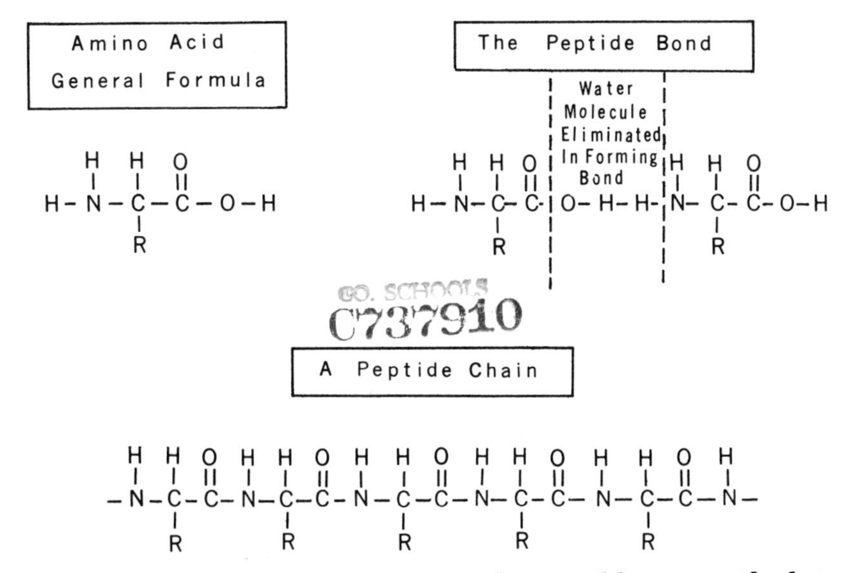

2–2 *The general formula of the amino acid unit, and how a peptide chain is formed from such units. The "R" side chain groups are shown all sticking out in the same direction, but actually they can stick out in any direction at right angles to the main chain.*

about 6000 amu, while human antibody molecules reach molecular weights of some 160,000 units. From the 14 notes and half notes of the musical scale, one can compose an endless variety of tunes; and from the 20 amino acids, nature creates a huge variety of polypeptide chains. In a polypeptide of only four units, the first residue can be any of 20 amino acids, and there are 20 possibilities for the second residue, and so on. Thus, there are 20 × 20 × 20 × 20, or 160,000, possible combinations. The potential number of different proteins becomes virtually unlimited when we consider that the average chain has around 600 residues and some contain tens of thousands.

The sequence of amino acids in a chain is called the primary structure of the protein. In some short chains, this may be the only structure possessed by the molecule. Commonly, however, a longer polypeptide will coil up something like a spring along considerable portions of its length. This type of coiling is called the alpha-helix, and it makes up the secondary structure of the protein. It is estimated that the protein in egg albumin has the alpha-helix structure along about 30 to 45 per cent of its length.

In addition to the secondary structure, a protein often has a tertiary structure, being folded and kinked in various ways. The tertiary structure of a protein is very difficult to discover, and only recently have computer-assisted analyses of how certain proteins scatter X rays enabled scientists to make models. Figure 2–3 shows the tertiary structure of the protein myoglobin, a protein found in high concentrations in the muscles of whales and seals. The molecule contains a single peptide chain of 151 amino acid residues enclosing a specialized molecular cluster known as a haem group. The straight portions of the structure are believed to be sections where the chain is coiled in the alpha-helix. The helix structure becomes uncoiled where the chain must make a bend. The diagram shows only the folding of the backbone of the polypeptide chain; the side groups have been left out. In reality, they fill the open spaces of the shape.

Not content with this kind of architectural marvel, nature in many proteins has provided a quaternary structure. This kind of structure is formed when several polypeptide chains become associated in a single huge molecule.

2–3 *The tertiary structure of myoglobin.*

The evidence seems to show that the protein chain is self-ordering. That is, given the same environment, two protein chains of the same composition will fold themselves up into identical structures. The particular structure which a protein will form depends not upon chance or some kind of template which the molecule follows but upon the kind and sequence of amino acid residues along its length.

This property of self-ordering has great significance when we consider the origin of life on our planet. It means that given a certain combination of molecular units, higher structures may automatically arise. This considerably reduces the part that blind chance may have played in life's beginning.

We have discussed the protein structure at such great

length not only because of the intrinsic interest of the subject, but because the structure of protein is closely related to its functions in the living cell. In a protein enzyme, the molecule's shape helps it carry out its job of joining together molecules or tearing them down. Enzymes are considered in more detail in Chapter 3.

Another significant job performed by proteins in protoplasm is that they serve as buffer compounds to help maintain the normal slight alkalinity of the cell.

There is a third great class of organic compounds—the lipids, which include the fats and oils, together with a number of other compounds. Mankind has been familiar with certain lipids since before the dawn of history. The first fats used by man were probably of animal origin. These were the tallows and greases, and were extracted from animal tissues by heating or boiling with water. Later, man learned how to extract fatty substances from plants, such as the olive oil the Egyptians used as lubricant for moving large stones and statues.

Lipids are almost insoluble in water, and animal and plant cells often store food in the form of droplets of fat or oil. When we overeat, the surplus food is stored in fatty tissue under our skins. In this adipose tissue, each cell is made up of a thin layer of protoplasm surrounding a large droplet of fat.

Such droplets are very concentrated sources of energy, for the fats and oils contain more than twice as many calories of food energy per ounce as do carbohydrates and proteins.

The fats and oils are chemically alike; the only basic difference between them is that fats are solid at room temperature while oils are liquid. Each fat or oil extracted from tissue is a complex mixture of compounds known as triglycerides. The basic formula of a triglyceride, or simple fat, is easy to understand. It is shown in Figure 2–4. Resembling a three-pronged fork, it consists of three long hydrocarbon chains attached to a molecule of glycerol. Each hydrocarbon chain is a compound of the type known as a fatty acid. When attached to the glycerol molecule, it is called a fatty acid residue. There are a number of fatty acids, and the triglycerides in a crude oil or fat extracted from tissue are varied in composition.

Perhaps the most important group of lipids are the phospholipids. These compounds, as their name implies, contain phosphorus. They are found in the cell membranes.

Like the simple fats, a typical phospholipid is composed of a glycerol with three branches. Two of these branches are

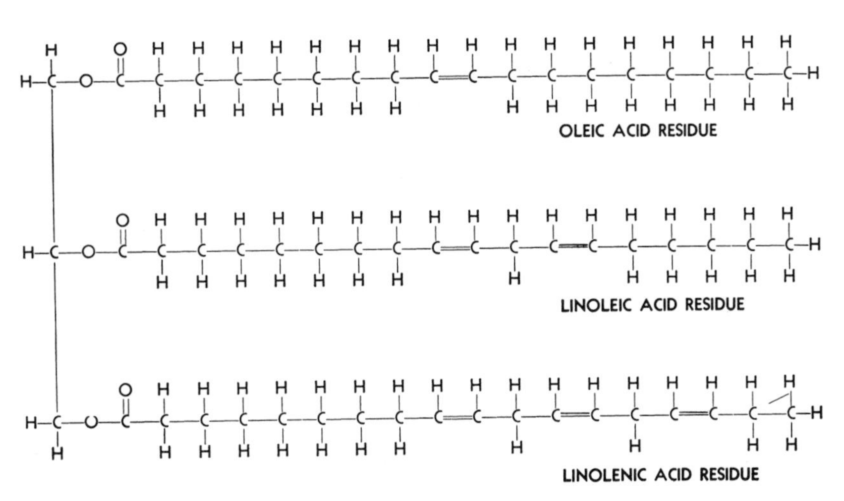

2–4 *The formula of one kind of simple fat molecule.*

fatty acids, like those involved in fat molecules. The third, however, is a chain containing both phosphorus and nitrogen.

We have covered three major classes of organic compounds. A fourth class—the nucleic acids—like the others is made up of giant molecules. These molecules carry the information needed for the proper functioning of the cell and also the units of heredity that are passed from cell generation to cell generation. However, we will delay consideration of these important compounds until the time when we take up the subject of cell reproduction.

3

PROTOPLASM AND THE LIVING CELL

We have spoken of water as the great solvent, and have mentioned that protoplasm is a solution of many substances. Protoplasm, however, exhibits some properties that most ordinary solutions do not have.

Microbiologists early noticed that protoplasm can change radically in consistency. At one moment, it can be an easily flowing substance that seems almost as fluid as water itself; at another instant, protoplasm becomes a gel that flows very thickly or not at all.

Although they cannot directly observe the protein molecules in protoplasm, scientists believe that this phenomenon is related to the presence of these molecules. The amino acids making up the protein molecule have unequal distributions of electrical charges. One area of an amino acid residue will be positively charged, while another will be negatively charged. These charged atomic groups attract ions and the dipolar water molecules, which become more or less bound to the protein. The proteins tend to form a three-dimensional network that binds ions and water molecules. When a large share of the water molecules are bound, the protoplasm becomes a semisolid, a gel. When the chemical balance shifts and causes corresponding changes in the electrical charges on the proteins, water molecules are freed and the protoplasm assumes the liquid state. The chemical shifts in protoplasm can be very rapid, causing an almost instantaneous change in the consistency of the material.

All the free particles in protoplasm are vibrating and moving about with varying speeds. The molecules of a substance introduced into the solution will partake of this motion. The random movements of the molecules will tend to disperse the substance, so that it becomes more or less uniformly spread through the cell. This process, called diffusion, is one of the major means of transport in protoplasm. Another important form of transport is protoplasmic streaming. The protoplasm liquefies partially, and currents carry materials from place to place.

One of the characteristics of life is growth, and we can observe individual cells growing in bulk as they absorb nutrients from the outside. However, when a cell reaches a certain size, rather than increasing in mass further, it splits in two, reproducing itself. Why can't a cell grow infinitely large, to make one of those protoplasmic monsters horror comic books portray? There are good reasons. A cell absorbs food substances, oxygen, and water from its environment, and these life necessities are transported to every part of the cell by diffusion. The amount of vital substances that the cell can absorb at any given moment depends greatly upon the *surface area* available for absorption, and the efficiency with which the substance can diffuse to all parts of the cell depends upon the cell's *mass.* The greater the surface area in relation to the mass, the more effectively the cell can absorb and distribute needed molecules.

Let us suppose that a cube 1 centimeter on each side has a mass of 1 gram. The cube will have 6 square centimeters of surface area, so the ratio of *surface area* to *mass* will be 6 to 1. Now, let us cut the cube into 1000 smaller cubes, each .1 centimeter on a side. Each of these smaller cubes will have a *surface area* to *mass* ratio of 600 to 1. When we come to a single-celled bacterium such as *Escherichia coli,* a common organism found in the human intestinal tract, the ratio of surface area to mass becomes 50,000 to 1. So, the smaller the cell, the more surface area it has in proportion to its mass, and the easier it is to absorb and distribute enough nutrients and other substances to support the cell. Conversely, the larger the cell, the more difficult it becomes for the cell to get needed materials. Evolution has produced larger and larger organisms, but these are made up of many cells. Organisms consisting of more than a few cells must have special provisions for getting adequate sustenance to each cell. The tiny fresh-water hydra, for example, has its cells arranged to form a cylindrical hollow sac. The walls of the sac are only two cells thick, so that needed molecules from the environment can easily reach all cells by diffusion. In most larger animals, there is a blood system to transport oxygen and food substances to the various tissues.

When we examine a cell under the light microscope, after having dyed it with special stains to make various structures stand out, we find that it has a definite structure (Figure 3–1). Perhaps the most prominent feature visible under the

3–1 A highly simplified diagram of some of the main structures of the cell. The size of some structures such as the mitochondria is exaggerated here.

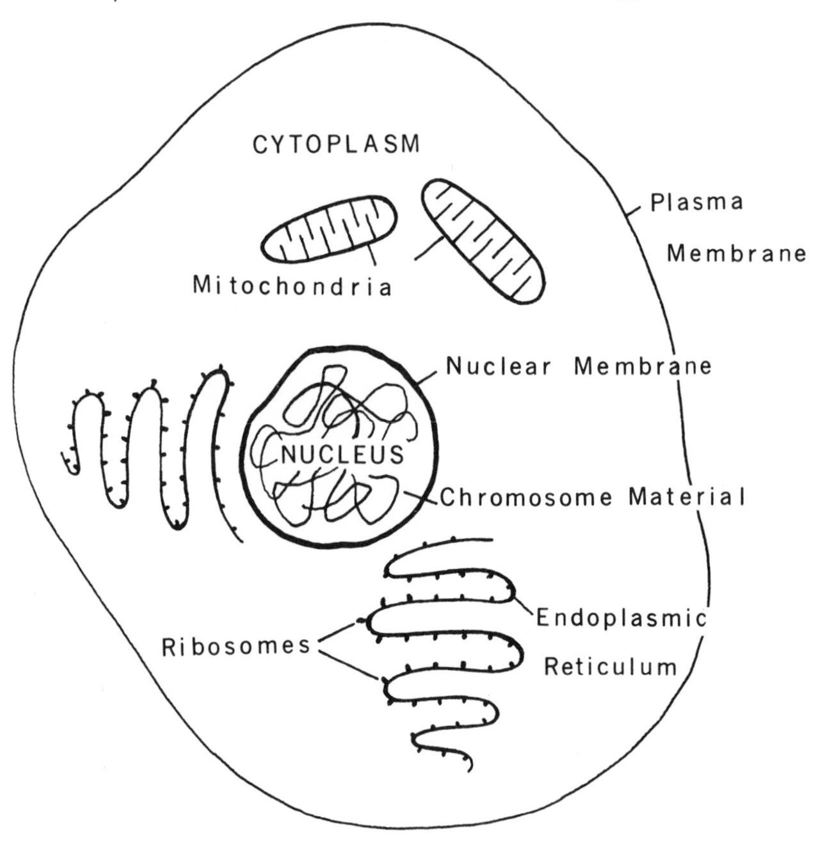

light microscope is the nucleus, a large blob in the center of the cell. Scientists have discovered that the nucleus is the control center from which the rest of the cell gets much of the information needed to carry out its activities.

The protoplasm outside the nucleus is known as the cytoplasm. Under the light microscope, many tiny particles can be observed in the cytoplasm, but it is impossible to make out any details of their structures. For many years, biologists were unable to learn much about these mysterious particles on the edge of visibility. Another puzzle concerned the boundary of the cell. The cytoplasm appeared to be restrained by an outer membrane, but the membrane itself was not visible under the light microscope. Some biologists doubted its existence.

The invention of the electron microscope in the 1930's changed all that. While the optical microscope can magnify effectively only 500 to 2000 times, the electron microscope is capable of effectively magnifying more than 100,000 times. The first electron microscopes were crude instruments, hardly much better than optical instruments. By the 1950's, however, the electron microscope was revealing a new world of minute detail within the cell. The mysterious particles in the cytoplasm turned out to have a definite complex architecture, and the cell indeed was found to have a limiting membrane. Meanwhile, advances in biochemistry were throwing light on many of the chemical reactions taking place in the cell, and it was found that some of them were localized in the cytoplasmic particles.

Biochemists have discovered that proteins play a key part

in all cell chemical processes. They serve as catalysts to promote desirable chemical reactions, such as the breaking down of food molecules.

A catalyst is a substance which promotes a certain chemical reaction but which itself is unchanged at the end of the reaction. Just about every important chemical reaction in the cell is associated with the presence of molecules of one or another protein. Such protein catalysts are called enzymes. The type of action carried out by enzymes may be observed by cutting an apple in two and leaving the halves exposed to the air. After a short time, the white cut surfaces of the fruit will begin to turn brown. The darkening is caused by the presence of enzymes that promote oxidation—the union of oxygen from the air with certain compounds in the apple. Similar darkening occurs when many other fresh fruits are cut and exposed to the air.

Biochemists have found ways to isolate specific enzymes and obtain them in purified form. One test of the purity of a chemical compound is whether or not the researcher can induce it to form crystals; crystallization is considered proof that the substance contains few impurities. Although an enzyme was isolated as early as 1897, the first one to be obtained in purified crystalline form was urease. The American researcher William Sumner performed this feat in 1926 and then chemically analyzed the enzyme. It turned out to be a protein, as have the many dozens of enzymes that have since been obtained in pure crystalline form. It is estimated that the *E. coli* cell contains some 2000 to 3000 enzymes. The names of these enzymes often give a clue to their functions.

With urease, for example, the "ase" ending shows that we are dealing with an enzyme. In this case, the enzyme catalyzes the breakdown of urea into carbon dioxide and ammonia. Many enzymes, like urease, break chemical compounds down into simpler units. Other enzymes promote unions between molecules.

In any case, an enzyme cannot promote a reaction that otherwise would be chemically impossible. What it does do is make it easier for the reaction to take place and thus speeds up the rate of reaction.

The substance upon which the enzyme works is called the substrate. It is believed, upon very firm evidence, that the enzyme and the substrate molecules make actual physical contact when the protein is carrying out its job. The union between the molecules is very brief and ends when the substrate has been transformed. A single molecule of enzyme can perform wonders of activity. The number of substrate molecules which are transformed by an enzyme molecule in one minute is the *turnover number* of that enzyme. Catalase, which converts hydrogen peroxide to water and oxygen, has a turnover number of 5,000,000.

The average enzyme is very specialized; it promotes one type of chemical reaction and no other. It appears that only a small part of the molecule, called the *active site*, comes into direct contact with the substrate. The rest of the molecule serves as support for the active site. In many enzymes, the active site can be separated from the main molecule by fairly mild chemical treatments. Such a separated portion is called a *prosthetic group* or a *coenzyme*. Vitamin B_6 is necessary to the body because it acts as a coenzyme for a number of enzyme molecules. Researchers find that an enzyme will not perform its job without the active site, nor will the active site do anything without the remainder of the enzyme molecule. Both appear to be necessary in catalyzing chemical reactions.

The enzymatic activity of proteins seems to be closely connected with their complicated molecular shapes. The active site of the enzyme very likely has a surface that fits only the substrate molecule, much as a lock is set to fit only one pattern of key. Let us assume that the enzyme's job is to split a substrate molecule. The substrate bumps against the active site, which has the correct molecular shape, chemical make-up, and electrical charge to attract the substrate. The substrate settles into the active site and enters into chemical union with it. As part of this union, the substrate molecule splits in two. The splitting changes the substrate fragments chemically so that they are no longer attracted to the active site. The two fragments drift away, leaving the active site exposed and ready to perform more work.

In 1969 two American scientific teams, which had been working independently, simultaneously announced a historic scientific achievement—the first test tube synthesis of an enzyme. The enzyme that they duplicated in the laboratory was ribonuclease, which breaks down the substance ribonucleic acid, or RNA. The enzyme is made up of 19 different kinds of amino acids strung together in a chain 124 units long.

The man-made chains, when placed in fluid, automatically folded into their proper three-dimensional shapes. When mixed with RNA, the synthetic substance broke down the RNA, just like the natural enzyme.

The scientists who did the research predict that enzyme synthesis will be a valuable research tool. For example, it is now possible to create enzymes in which selected amino acids are changed and see how the substitutions affect the functioning of the enzymes.

One thing that strikes us when we study cells is the high degree of order found in them. They are not simply bags of random compounds; they are made up of many highly organized subunits, ranging from protein molecules to various specialized structures such as membranes. Now, many natural processes are operating to create disorder in the cell: natural molecular vibrations from time to time tear apart important chemical bonds; radiation from space and from radioactive materials in the earth's crust is constantly zipping through cells and causing damage to molecules, etc. We know that this tendency toward disorder is an inherent property of natural systems. The scientific term for disorder is *entropy;* and the second law of thermodynamics states that the amount of entropy in natural systems always tends to increase. That is, it tends to increase unless work is done on the system to restore the order. This work requires the expenditure of energy.

Cells are constantly engaged in repair work. When a protein molecule in the body becomes damaged and incapable of functioning, the molecule is broken down into simple compounds which are excreted from the body. Also, the body apparently breaks down any protein molecule after a certain time as part of its normal metabolic processes. These proteins must be replaced by building new ones from food substances. To do this construction work, the cell needs energy. This energy is obtained by breaking down food compounds into water and carbon dioxide. In both plant and animal cells, the main food is usually carbohydrates, the starches and sugars.

When a plant synthesizes a carbohydrate such as glucose, the energy obtained from sunlight is imprisoned, as it were, in the form of chemical energy. This means that the energy of sunlight is used to bring certain atoms close together with enough force so that they will form chemical bonds. Like compressed springs, the chemical bonds hold stored energy, which is released when the bonds are broken or rearranged by enzymes as the molecule is used as food. Usually, in cellular reactions, a share of the energy is used in creating new bonds and chemical compounds, while the rest appears in the form of greater energy of motion of atoms and molecules. Such atomic and molecular motion is *heat.* Your body's warmth is a result of some of the chemical energy in food being transformed into heat energy, i.e., molecular motion.

An organism needs some way to store the chemical energy released when foodstuffs are broken down. This job, scientists have found, is performed by the key compound adenosine triphosphate, or ATP. ATP stores energy until it is needed for such tasks as building up compounds or muscle contraction. The ATP molecule is formed by the addition of a phosphate group to a molecule of adenosine diphosphate, or ADP. The energy stored in the bond is released by the removal of the phosphate group. So, energy is stored by conversion of ADP to ATP, and released by conversion of ATP to ADP.

In both plants and animals, the main source of energy is the simple sugar glucose. In plants, excess glucose may be stored by linking the sugars together to form long starch molecules; the same process is carried out in animals to form glycogen, or animal starch. When glucose is needed, the starch or the glycogen is broken down into its sugar subunits, which then are further broken down to release energy for transfer to ATP.

The breakdown of glucose takes place in a series of steps, with each step promoted by a specific enzyme. The first steps do not require the presence of oxygen and are called fermentation. Some microorganisms rely just upon fermentation for their energy and thus do not require atmospheric oxygen for their existence. As a matter of fact, oxygen kills many of these organisms. Since geologists believe that the earth had little or no oxygen in its air when life first arose, the earliest organisms probably relied upon fermentation to release energy from glucose or other compounds.

Less than one tenth of the chemical energy stored in glucose is set free in fermentation, however. The remainder of the energy can be freed only by a series of reactions that require oxygen to complete. Higher plants and animals all depend upon this second stage for most of their energy, and thus all require a source of oxygen. However, a cell can meet its energy needs for a limited time by fermentation when its oxygen supply is inadequate.

In fermentation, about nine different types of enzymes are needed to break a glucose molecule into two molecules of pyruvic acid. In the process, two ATP molecules donate their energy, and four molecules of ATP are formed, making a surplus of two ATP molecules. This surplus stored energy is available for other tasks in the cell. (The detailed steps involved in fermentation are given in Appendix B of this book, for the reader who likes to see "how it works.")

The enzymes involved in fermentation are believed to be scattered more or less at random through the cytoplasm of the cell. This is not true of those connected with the next series of reactions, involving oxygen, called respiration. Respiration appears to take place in the cytoplasmic particles known as mitochondria. The enzymes are thought to be located on the membranes of each mitochondrion. They are arranged somewhat in assembly-line fashion, so that a molecule undergoing the process passes from one enzyme directly to the next.

The various steps in respiration have been figured out through careful experiment, although some details are not completely clear yet. Respiration begins where fermentation leaves off, with pyruvic acid. The end result is carbon dioxide and water. While the fermentation of a single glucose molecule involves creation of a surplus of 2 ATP molecules, the reactions of respiration create a total of some 36 additional ATP molecules. So respiration is the more effective process of getting energy.

The cell can break down compounds other than glucose to release energy, including fats and proteins. These are secondary sources of energy under most conditions, however.

We have mentioned that the world's carbohydrates are manufactured by plants. Whereas respiration breaks down glucose into water and carbon dioxide, photosynthesis builds up glucose from water and CO_2. Photosynthesis involves this reaction:

$$6CO_2 + 6H_2O + \text{light energy} \rightarrow C_6H_{12}O_6 + 6O_2$$

Each year, the plants of the globe "fix" about 100,000,000,000 tons of carbon in organic form from the CO_2 of the atmosphere. Thus, while both animals and plants continuously give off CO_2 as a waste product, the plants take it up again and prevent its accumulation in the atmosphere. Notice that oxygen is a product of this reaction, along with sugar. Most scientists now believe that our Earth's supply of atmospheric oxygen was created largely by plants after the process of photosynthesis was evolved.

The oxygen produced by plants is used up by animals in respiration, so the vital gases of oxygen and carbon dioxide continuously cycle between plants and animals, forming one very important part of the delicate balance of nature.

4

THE MEMBRANES OF THE CELL

THE CELL NEEDS to be separated from its environment in some way, else its contents would quickly leak away. The necessary boundary is formed by a thin membrane enclosing the cytoplasm like a sac (Figure 3–1). This plasma membrane is too thin to be visible except under the electron microscope.

The passage of water and other substances in and out of the cell is regulated by the plasma membrane. In plants from the bacteria upward, the membrane is enclosed in a tough rigid wall that maintains the cell's shape. If a number of rod-shaped bacteria are suspended in a liquid and their cell walls are dissolved chemically, each cell loses its rod shape and rounds up into a sphere. If the plasma membrane is then ruptured, the cell contents leak out into the liquid and the cell disintegrates. So the plasma membrane clearly is essential to the maintenance of the cell. Whether or not the first *life* required such membranes is not clear, but the first cells probably could not arise without them.

The plasma membrane is not simply a passive container. First of all, it is semipermeable. It allows small molecules to enter or leave the cell, while preventing the passage of large ones. For instance, the plasma membrane can allow passage of small sugar molecules into or out of a cell, while preventing passage of those same molecules when they are linked together in starch molecules. This is why the various giant molecules so essential to life remain within the cell and do not leak out, while the cell nonetheless is able to absorb water and food and to excrete wastes. Secondly, much of this molecular traffic through the membrane involves *active transport;* that is, the cell expends energy to bring in certain molecules and get rid of others. Perhaps the major example of active transport is the movement of various ions across the membrane. The reader will recall from Chapter 1 that certain atoms or molecular groups can become electrically charged. One important ion involved in life processes is the positively charged sodium atom. In the body, the fluid bathing the cell contains sodium ions. Sodium ions are constantly passing into the cell. We would expect the concentration of sodium within the cell to rise steadily until it matched the concentration outside the cell. This does not happen, however. The cell actively pumps out sodium ions so that their concentration within the membrane is always lower than their concentration outside.

With positively charged potassium ions, however, the active transport system keeps the ionic concentration much higher within the cell than outside it.

Some of the molecular traffic across the membrane can be explained by assuming that the membrane has many tiny holes, or pores, through which small molecules can move by random diffusion. However, such pores have never been actually observed in the plasma membrane, even under great magnification. And this hypothesis does not account for the phenomenon of active transport. A number of possible mechanisms for active transport have been proposed. It may be that certain molecules are transported through the membrane "piggyback" on carrier molecules. But no one knows for sure, and much additional research will be required before our questions are satisfactorily answered.

Chemical analysis of the plasma membrane shows that it is rich in phospholipids. One source of membrane for analysis is red blood cells. The red blood cell lacks a nucleus; it basically is a membrane envelope filled with cytoplasm that is almost entirely made up of the protein hemoglobin. The hemoglobin can be leached out of red blood cells, leaving plasma membrane "ghosts" suitable for chemical analysis. The ghosts contain equal amounts of lipid and protein, and this is a clue that the cell membrane is made up of both kinds of molecules.

The reader may recall from Chapter 2 that phospholipids have a structure similar to fat molecules. The typical phospholipid is made up of two fatty acid chains linked to a third chain containing phosphorus and nitrogen. The structure of one of the phospholipids found in the "ghosts" of red blood cells from cattle is shown in Figure 4–1.

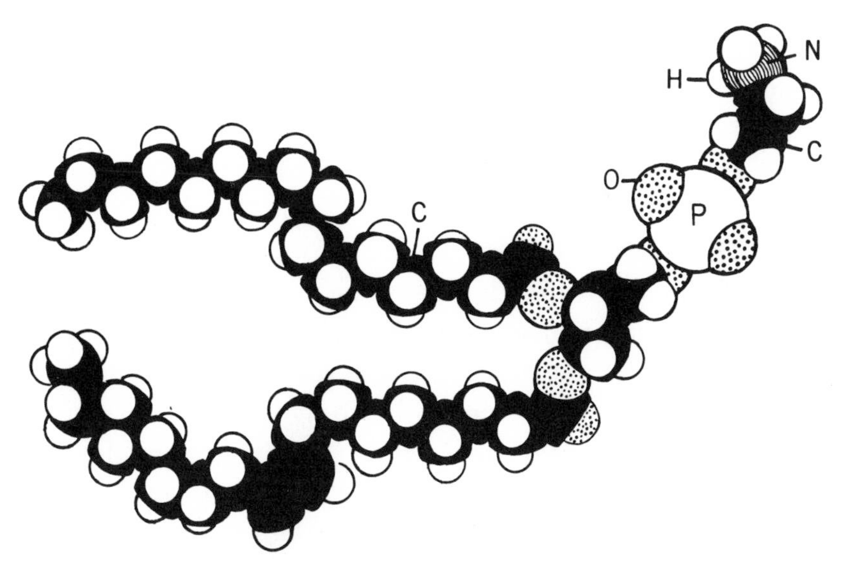

4–1 A drawing of a model of a phospholipid molecule. The various types of atoms in the molecule are labeled.

A very significant property of the phospholipid molecule is that it has a "split personality," chemically speaking. The two fatty acid residues are hydrophobic; that is, they resist being dissolved in water. The phosphorus-containing chain, however, is hydrophilic, or water-loving. It is attracted to water. When phospholipids are present in an open container of water, they tend to gather as a sheet at the surface, with the hydrophilic chain sticking down into the water and the hydrophobic portion of the molecule sticking up into the air, away from the water. When there is no air-water interface, the phospholipid molecules tend to clump together in clusters, called micelles, with their hydrophilic ends projecting out into the water and the other ends pointing inward, away from the water. Thus, in both situations, the phospholipid molecules tend to assemble together automatically to form ordered arrays (Figure 4–2).

In 1925, the researchers Gortner and Rendel extracted the lipid from a sample of red blood cells and dissolved the lipid in benzene. Then they spread the solution on the surface of water in a shallow trough. The surface was a water-air interface. The benzene evaporated, leaving a sheet of lipid at the interface. The researchers took a thread and drew it across the surface from one edge of the trough. The layer of lipid was compressed into a smaller area. They continued drawing the thread across the surface until the lipid layer offered resistance to further compression. This indicated to them that

4–2 How phospholipid molecules can form a sheet or micelle.

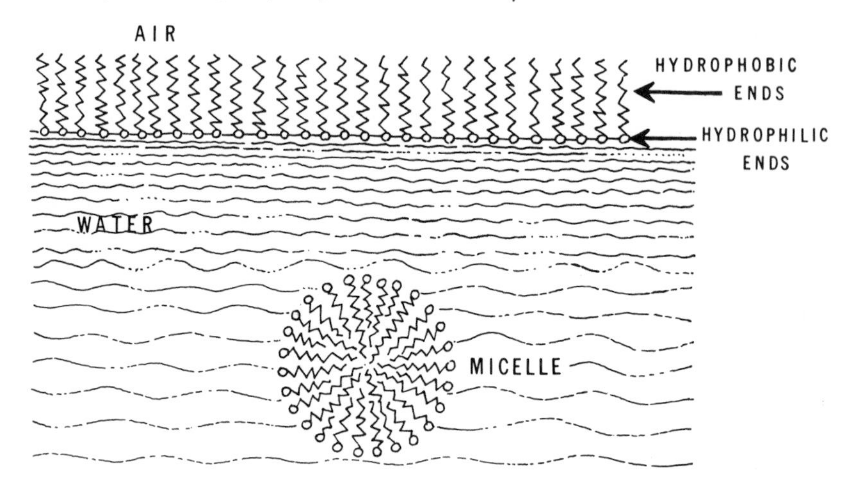

the molecules of lipid were packed together as shown in Figure 4–2, with the water-loving ends of the molecules downward and the water-repelling ends projecting upward. The molecules offered resistance to being crowded into a smaller area because they were already as close-packed as they could be without the layer's buckling. The scientists measured the area of the one-molecule-thick layer they had formed. They knew the total surface area of the red cells in the sample from which they had obtained the lipid. Simple

4–3 *Membrane models. "A" represents the Gortner-Rendel model, and "B" the Danielli-Davson model, with protein bound to the outer surfaces of the phospholipid layers.*

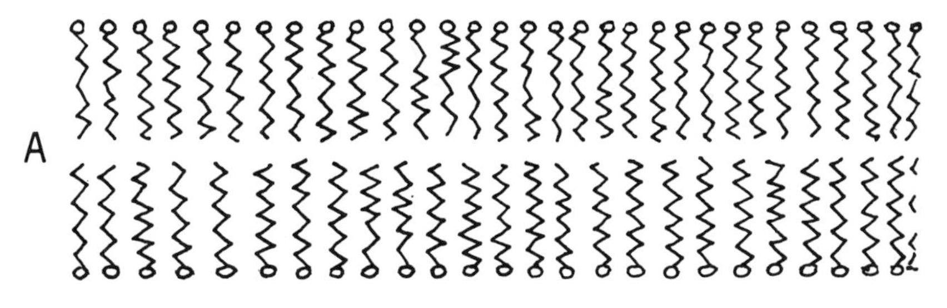

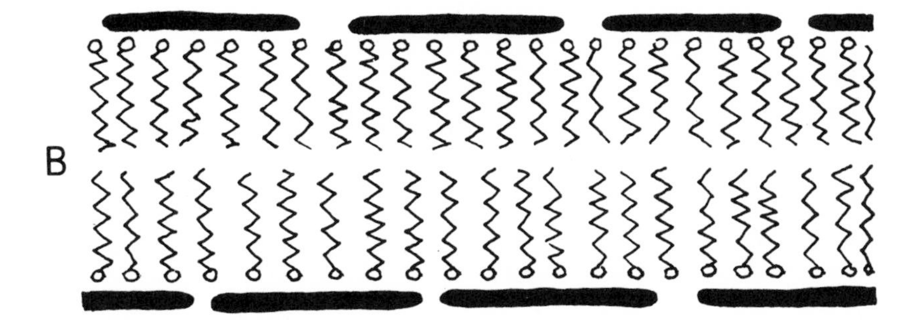

arithmetic showed them that there was enough lipid to form a layer two molecules thick over each red cell. They suggested that the plasma membrane in red blood cells might be made up of such a two-molecule layer, as shown in Figure 4–3.

We have mentioned that red cell "ghosts" contain protein. In 1935, Danielli and Davson proposed an addition to the membrane model. They said that certain properties of cell membranes, such as the fact that they are elastic and stretchable, made it likely that the protein is bound to the outermost surfaces of the lipid layers. Figure 4–3 also shows what came to be called the Danielli model of the membrane.

To study cells under the electron microscope, a sample of tissue is first treated with a stain containing atoms of a metal, such as osmium. The metal atoms attach themselves to certain cell structures such as membranes, thus rendering these structures more opaque to electrons than the rest of the cell. Then the specimen is embedded in a block of plastic and a very, very thin slice is cut using a sharp glass or diamond knife. The slice, or section as it is called, is mounted on a wire grid and placed in the electron microscope so that the beam of electrons will pass through it. When the electron beam is passed through the thin section, the parts of the cells that have been stained with the metal block electrons, and thus these structures appear darker in the final image.

Most cells turn out to have a number of membrane structures in addition to the plasma membrane bounding the cell. For example, the typical cell has a complicated series of membranes winding through the protoplasm, called the endoplasmic reticulum. There also is a membrane enclosing the cell nucleus.

Under high magnification in the electron microscope, these membranes appear to share a similar structure. Each appears to be a kind of molecular sandwich made up of two dark outer layers enclosing a third layer. In 1959, the American scientist J. David Robertson, who was then working in London, published an article in which he proposed that biological membranes share a common structure. This proposed structure, called the unit membrane, closely resembles the model suggested by Danielli and Davson. The sandwich structure visible in electron micrographs is interpreted like this: The inner part of the sandwich is made up of a double layer of phospholipid molecules with their "water-loving" ends pointing outward. The outer dark layers visible in the electron micrographs are interpreted to be nonlipid molecules, such as protein and carbohydrates, that are bound chemically to the ends of lipid molecules.

The unit membrane theory has won wide acceptance among biochemists and molecular biologists. However, it has been questioned by some researchers who believe that there is evidence that cell membranes may not all fit the unit membrane structure.

Many cells have an additional coat of material outside the plasma membrane to help support and give shape to the cell. Quite often, when a biologist or physiologist refers to the cell membrane, he is speaking both of the plasma membrane and the outermost cell coat. In animals, the cell coat serves as a cement to help bind cells together into tissues. In plants, the outer layer is a tough and rigid *cell wall* that is almost always composed of cellulose. This cell wall provides the rigidity we note in plants.

Scientists believe that, given the proper phospholipid and protein molecules, a membrane probably has the ability to assemble itself, much as the phospholipids at an air-water interface gather spontaneously into an ordered sheet. Here again, the important principle of self-assembly appears in connection with a biological structure. If the proper molecules were present in the right environment on the early Earth, it is likely that biologically active membranes might have arisen spontaneously.

5

REPRODUCTION

THE PROTEIN ENZYMES largely determine what chemical reactions will take place in the cell. What determines what enzymes the cell will have? Related to this query is another: How is this information passed from an organism to its descendants? The nucleus has been found to play a key role in these functions.

Although a cell can survive for a time after its nucleus has been destroyed, it eventually dies because new enzymes are not being manufactured to take the place of those which wear out. Thus, the nucleus apparently contains some information or mechanism needed for the manufacture of enzyme proteins. The nucleus also is deeply involved in heredity—the passing of information from an organism to its progeny. The simplest type of reproduction is cell reproduction, in which the cell splits into two complete units. Single-celled organisms reproduce in this way. Also, many of the cells in our body divide periodically in order to replace damaged or dead cells.

The role of the nucleus in heredity was only slowly understood. In 1879, the German cell researcher Walther Flemming found that certain dyes stained areas in the cell nucleus but left the rest of the cell unstained. The material in the nucleus that could absorb the color he called chromatin (from the Greek *chroma,* meaning color). The use of these dyes helped Flemming study the process of cell division. He stained sections of growing tissue containing many cells in various stages of dividing. The use of the stain killed the cells, but since the cells were in many different stages of division, he could piece together a continuous "story" of how a single cell goes through the process. Before the cell starts division, its nucleus is a well-defined body enclosed in its membrane. The chromatin inside is in small clumps. When the time comes for the cell to divide, the chromatin begins to form thick threads, or squiggly rods, which received the name of *chromosomes* from the German scientist Wilhelm Gottfried Waldeyer in 1888. In modern times, electron microscopy has revealed that the chromatin is always in the form of threads, but most of the time these threads are too fine to be observable as such under the ordinary light microscope. As the threads thicken into chromosome rods, each somehow duplicates itself, so that we soon have a collection of chromosome pairs. During this time, the nuclear membrane has dissolved, allowing the cytoplasm and the nuclear material to mix freely. The chromosome pairs line up along the "equator" of the cell, and then each pair splits apart. One set of chromosomes migrates toward one side of the cell, while the other set moves to the other side. Figure 5–1 illustrates this process. Meanwhile, the cell becomes pinched in the middle and eventually divides into two cells, each with its complete set of chromosomes. A new nuclear membrane forms around the chromosomes in each cell, and they "dissolve" into random clumps of chromatin again.

While single cells reproduce by dividing, most higher plants and animals make use of sexual reproduction to produce new offspring. In this form of reproduction, a special cell from the male, called a sperm, unites with a cell from the female, called the egg. These merge into one cell, the start of a new organism (Figure 5–2). It turns out that the sperm carries only half the usual number of chromosomes found in the cells of the father. And the egg carries only half the number of chromosomes found ordinarily in each of the mother's cells. When the sperm and egg merge, the new cell gains a

5–1 *Cell division shown schematically and not to scale.*

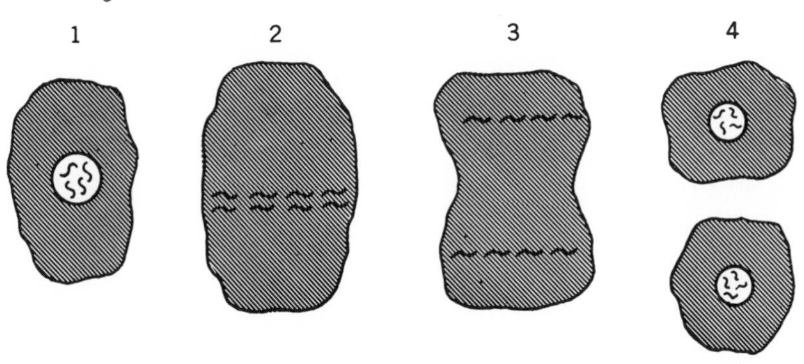

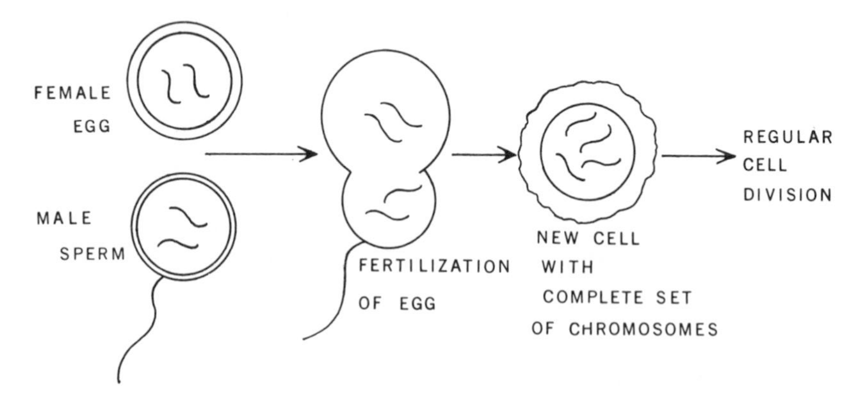

5–2 *A highly simplified representation of the fusion between the male sperm cell and the female egg cell. Not to scale.*

full set of chromosomes, half from the father and half from the mother. The cell, called a fertilized egg, then begins to divide in the usual way. It becomes two cells, then four, then eight, and so on, until a new organism is formed. Each cell in this offspring has a full set of chromosomes, half of them duplicates of those gained from the mother and half duplicates of those from the father.

It is a common observation that a human baby inherits characteristics from both its mother and its father. It may have its father's brown eyes and its mother's shape of nose. When biologists saw how a fertilized egg gets half of its chromosomes from the father and half from the mother, they wondered if the chromosomes might not be the carriers of hereditary information. Several researchers suggested this before the end of the nineteenth century, and it gradually became standard scientific doctrine in the following decades.

Chemical studies of the nucleus also were going forward during the nineteenth century. The Swiss researcher Friedrich Miescher was the first scientist to attempt to isolate the nucleus by chemical methods. He worked with the white blood cells found in pus. The scientist discovered that dilute hydrochloric acid dissolves most of the cell material, leaving the bare nuclei. He chemically analyzed the nuclei and discovered a phosphorus-containing material which did not appear to be protein, carbohydrate, or any other known cell substance. He called this substance *nuclein.* In later research on salmon sperm, he discovered that it had acid properties. In 1899, the biochemist Richard Altmann suggested that the substance be called *nucleic acid,* and this name was generally adopted.

Researchers found that nucleic acid was the material in chromosomes that accepted the stains that made these bodies visible under the microscope. And in 1884, the German scientist Oskar Hertwig, who had performed some of the classic research on fertilization, declared his belief that nucleic acid not only is the substance responsible for fertilization but also carries the hereditary information.

This concept was widely accepted but later fell into doubt because of certain findings that seemed to be evidence against it. For one thing, nucleic acid is not the only material found in the chromosomes. The chromosomes also contain protein, usually of the kind known as histone, and there could be no absolute certainty that the hereditary information wasn't carried by the protein, rather than the nucleic acid. Also, scientists had come to appreciate more fully the key role of proteins in the cell. It became clear that the basic role of the chromosomes is to carry the information needed to construct the many different enzymes of the cell; "heredity" is simply the passing of this information from one generation to the next. Researchers had learned that an enzyme is made up of roughly 20 different kinds of amino acids strung together in chains of hundreds or thousands of units, each chain made up of a precise sequence of amino acids. Now, chemical analysis of nucleic acid showed that, like most larger cell molecules, it is made up of smaller molecules linked together. However, there are only four different kinds of subunits in a typical nucleic acid molecule, compared to 20 in protein. And the early methods of isolating nucleic acid produced only short chains of such subunits. It was difficult for scientists to see how such a short, apparently simple, molecule could carry the information needed for directing the synthesis of an enzyme. Many of them felt that the proteins linked to the nucleic acids were more likely to have the necessary complexity to perform the job. Scientific opinion shifted toward the view that nucleic acid was not the hereditary material.

However, in the 1940's certain new experimental results forced a re-evaluation. It was shown that nucleic acid from one strain of bacteria, when taken up by another strain, caused the second type of bacterium to acquire some of the characteristics of the first strain. More evidence came from the study of viruses. A virus appears to be an inert, lifeless particle until it enters a living cell. Then it forces the cell to produce new viruses, which escape and can infect other cells. When a virus enters a cell, it acts like a chromosome and causes the cell to produce the enzymes necessary to make copies of the virus. Close examination of a virus reveals that it consists of nucleic acid wrapped in a protein coat. Scientists found that the protein coat is not at all necessary to the operation of reproduction, once the microbe is inside the cell. Nucleic acid taken from tobacco mosaic viruses was rubbed into scratches on the leaves of tobacco plants. Some entered the cells and caused them to manufacture new viruses, complete with protein coats. Thus, as far as viruses were concerned, nucleic acid turned out to be *the* hereditary substance. If viruses, why not cells?

Meanwhile, gentler methods of isolating nucleic acid resulted in obtaining long giant molecules that approached the proteins in length. This overcame one of the earlier objections: it seemed that the nucleic acid molecule might be complex enough, after all, to serve as a storehouse of information.

The nucleic acid found in the chromosomes is called deoxyribonucleic acid, or DNA for short. There is another variety found in the neighborhood of the chromosomes and also outside the nucleus. This is named ribonucleic acid, or RNA. It cooperates chemically with the DNA in directing cell operations.

The building-block molecules of nucleic acid are known as nucleotides. Each nucleotide consists of three sections: an atomic group called a base linked to a sugar molecule that is connected in turn to a phosphate group:

PHOSPHATE
+
BASE + SUGAR

DNA has four types of nucleotides, each with a different base. The names of the bases are adenine, cytosine, guanine, and thymine. These names often are abbreviated to A, C, G, and T. The nucleotides can be linked together through their phosphate and sugar groups, something like this:

```
     Phosphate
         +
  A + Sugar
         +
     Phosphate
         +
  T + Sugar
         +
     Phosphate
         +
  C + Sugar
```

The bases can occur in any order along this chain. Unlike the other giant molecules of the cell, each DNA molecule consists of *two* chains cross-linked to each other. The two chains are connected through their bases like this:

```
P               P
+               +
S + A + T + S
+               +
P               P
+               +
S + G + C + S
+               +
P               P
+               +
S + T + A + S
+               +
P               P
+               +
S + T + A + S
```

Thus, the DNA molecule resembles a ladder with rungs made up of linked bases. Ordinarily, this ladder is represented in print simply by the bases, with the sugar and phosphate groups omitted for sake of simplicity:

A + T
G + C
T + A
T + A

We find that an A base is always linked to a T, and vice versa. Every G is always linked with a C, and vice versa. Also, the ladder is twisted so that the two chains form a spiral. This shape is called the double helix.

The DNA double helix has the unique power of being able to duplicate itself in the presence of suitable enzymes. When the cell is ready to divide, each DNA thread copies itself, and thus the cell gains a double set of chromosomes (Figure 5–3). How this is done is explained in detail in Appendix C.

DNA also carries in chemical form the information needed for the manufacture of proteins. It does this through serving as a template, or mold, for the construction of RNA molecules. The RNA molecule is also made up of nucleotides. These are slightly different in chemical composition from DNA nucleotides. There are four types of RNA nucleotides. Three of them carry the same bases as are found in DNA: adenine, cytosine, and guanine. The fourth nucleotide, however, has the base uracil, instead of thymine. Another difference between RNA and DNA is that RNA usually is found in single strands, as opposed to two chains linked together. While almost all the

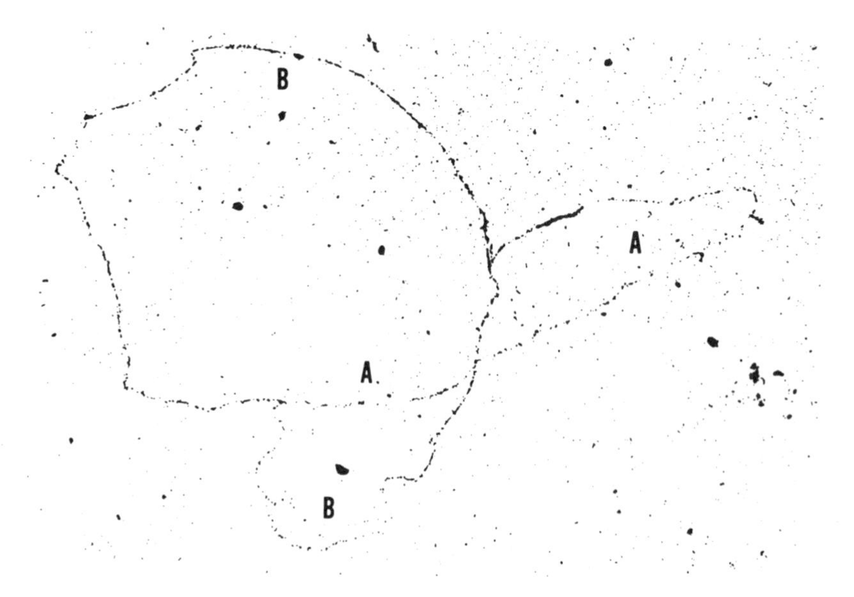

5–3 *The circular DNA strand (B) of the* E. COLI *bacterium caught in the process of reproducing itself and forming a new strand (A). In* E. COLI *the DNA molecule is joined at its ends to form a closed loop.*

cell's DNA is found inside the nucleus, RNA is found both in the nucleus and outside of it.

The DNA in the chromosomes serves as a template for the construction of RNA molecules known as messenger RNA. The mRNA migrates to the cytoplasm, where it is found associated with particles called ribosomes. Here, the mRNA molecules serve as templates for the construction of protein enzymes. The sequence goes like this:

$$\text{DNA} \rightarrow \text{mRNA} \rightarrow \text{protein}$$

The American scientist James Watson, who helped unravel the structure of DNA, calls this formula the "central dogma" of modern biology. Scientists at present believe that this sequence of operations is found in all cells. Appendix C outlines the sequence in detail.

It should be noted that each step in the process requires the presence of enzymes. So the sequence is actually circular: in order to direct the manufacture of proteins, the DNA requires the presence of certain proteins. As we shall see, this puts scientists in somewhat of a dilemma in discussing the origin of life. Which came first, the protein or the nucleic acid? Or did they arise simultaneously? In that case, how did the activities of these molecules become coordinated?

6

EARLY IDEAS ABOUT THE ORIGIN OF LIFE

EARLIER CULTURES, lacking firm scientific knowledge about our Earth and its past, invented various explanations about the origin of life. These usually began with the creation of the universe and culminated in the appearance of man. Some of these explanations were religious. The Hebrews said that God created the world from primeval chaos and then created the various orders of plants and animals. This part of creation took five days. On the sixth day, God molded man from the dust and breathed life into him. Other explanations left God out and visualized life's arising from nonlife by a sort of natural materialistic evolution. Some of these theories were almost modern in their outlook. The ancient Greek thinker Anaximander, who lived in Ionia from 611 B.C. to 545 B.C., noted that fossil remains of fish and other water creatures are often found on dry land. He felt that this showed that most of the world must have been at one time covered by water. Life arose from the moist slime left by the evaporation of water, he suggested. The first creatures must have had a hard covering, he thought, to guard themselves against being evaporated, too, by the sun's rays.

Both early religious and nonreligious theories usually saw creation as taking a certain amount of time and following a definite order of events. First there is some sort of chaos out of which the world is formed. Then lower living things arise, and finally man appears. It is interesting that a similar sequence of events is suggested by modern scientific theories about the origin of the universe and of life.

When scraps of meat and other garbage are left to decay in the open air, fly maggots often appear on the rotting material. Leave a bundle of old rags in an outbuilding and one is likely to find them later inhabited by mice. From classical times almost up to the present, such observations led people to believe in "spontaneous generation" of life from nonliving materials. Even people who accepted the idea of Divine Creation also often believed that spontaneous generation of flies, mice, and other creatures was an everyday occurrence. The Belgian physician Johann Baptista van Helmont (1577–1644), who is noted for his researches on gases and on plant nutrition, gives instructions for creating mice by stuffing a dirty undergarment into a jar containing wheat and leaving it there for about 21 days. The wheat eventually turns into mice, Van Helmont says, and "what is more remarkable, the mice

. . . are neither weanlings nor sucklings nor premature but they jump out fully formed."

A blow against the theory of spontaneous generation was struck by the Italian biologist Francesco Redi, who lived from 1626 to 1697. Redi exposed meat to the air in jars.

Flies were attracted to the jars. Some of the jars were completely open to the air. In these jars the flies were able to land on the meat. Eventually, maggots appeared. However, some of the jars were covered by gauze, preventing the flies from reaching the meat. No maggots developed in the meat but some appeared on the gauze. This convinced Redi that maggots are not produced directly from decaying meat, but arise from eggs laid by flies.

About this same time, the Dutchman Antony van Leewenhoek was reporting on his revolutionary observations of microorganisms through his homemade microscopes. Leewenhoek, and the researchers who followed him, discovered that a world exists of tiny organisms invisible to ordinary vision. These creatures appear everywhere: in stagnant pond water; in the white material that accumulates between human teeth; in the soil.

Perhaps larger creatures cannot arise by spontaneous generation, some people argued, but certainly these tiny organisms might easily arise that way. A scientific controversy arose that was not settled conclusively until a series of brilliant experiments in the nineteenth century by the French microbiologist Louis Pasteur. In these experiments, Pasteur demonstrated that microbes never arise from materials that are completely germfree. They are found only in substances which have been exposed in some way to germs.

In reporting the results of his work, in 1864, Pasteur said: "There is no condition known today in which you can affirm that microscopic beings come into the world without germs, without parents like themselves. Those who allege it have been the sport of illusions, of ill-made experiments, vitiated by errors which they have not been able to perceive and have not known how to avoid."

Pasteur's work was invaluable in clearing the air. Now, when scientists ran across any kind of organism, they could confidently assume that the creature was not a mysterious product of spontaneous generation but was the offspring of an organism like itself.

The idea that "life comes only from life" tended to become a scientific dogma. The British physicist William Thompson (Lord Kelvin) wrote: "The impossibility of spontaneous generation, at any time whatever, must be considered as firmly established as the law of universal gravitation."

The dogma, however, came into conflict with the growing geological and biological evidence that life on our planet had a definite beginning many millions of years ago. Fossils showed that present-day higher plants and animals arose from simpler organisms in the distant past. The British scientist Charles Darwin wrote, in his historic book *The Origin of Species:* "I believe that animals are descended from at most only four or five progenitors, and plants from an equal or lesser number. Analogy would lead me one step further, namely, to the belief that all animals and plants are descended from one prototype . . . All living things have much in common, in their chemical composition, their cellular structure, their laws of growth, and their liability to injurious influences. We see this even in so trifling a fact as that the same poisons often similarly affect plants and animals; or that the poison secreted by the gall-fly produces monstrous growths on the wild rose or oak-tree. With all organic beings, excepting perhaps some of the very lowest, sexual reproduction seems to be essentially similar . . . If we look even to the two main divisions, namely, to the animal and vegetable kingdoms —certain low forms are so far intermediate in character that naturalists have disputed to which kingdom they should be referred . . . Therefore . . . it does not seem incredible that, from some such low and intermediate form, both animals and plants may have developed; and, if we admit this, we must likewise admit that all the organic beings which have ever lived on this earth may be descended from some one primordial form . . . and that, whilst this planet has gone cycling on according to the fixed law of gravity, from so simple a beginning endless forms most beautiful and most wonderful have been, and are being evolved."

If "life comes only from life," how did Darwin's "one primordial form" arise? To those accepting Divine Creation, this question did not pose any problem. Other individuals proposed that life was a sort of vital force that, like gravitation, had existed from the beginnings of the universe. Perhaps the germ of life arrived on Earth from another planet, they suggested. This theory was first proposed by H. E. Richter. He suggested that microorganisms could be carried through space on particles of dust cast off by celestial bodies. Such a germ, arriving on Earth, might be the forebear of all present organisms. The "Panspermia" theory, as it was called, won the support of many men of science, including the German physicist Hermann von Helmholtz and the Englishman William Thompson. Astronomers of the time thought that meteorites falling on Earth might be the remains of a broken-up planet, and Helmholtz proposed that earthly life arose from simple life forms that arrived via meteorite. It was found that light exerts a small but measurable pressure, and the Swedish chemist and physicist Svante Arrhenius suggested that bacteria might have been driven through space to our planet by the pressure of light from the sun or other stars.

Some scientists, however, argued that life on our world probably arose from inorganic materials in the dim past. Why doesn't spontaneous generation occur nowadays? Perhaps because conditions now are different than they were then.

Darwin, in *The Origin of Species,* wrote of life's "having been originally breathed by the Creator into a few forms or into one." However, his reference to "the Creator" seems to have been aimed at quieting possible criticism from religious people about his theories. In 1863, several years after the book was published, Darwin wrote to a scientific friend that he regretted "having truckled to public opinion" by referring to Divine Creation when what he actually meant was that life appeared by "some wholly unknown process."

What that process was, Darwin did not feel competent to say. "It is mere rubbish," he told his friend, "thinking at present about the origin of life; one might as well think of the origin of matter."

In 1871, he did point out one reason why spontaneous generation no longer could produce new life forms. In a letter to another acquaintance, he wrote: "It is often said that all the conditions for the first production of a living organism are now present, which could ever have been present. But if (and oh! what a big if!) we could conceive in some warm little pond, with all sorts of ammonia and phosphoric salts, light, heat, electricity, etc., present, that a proteine compound was chemically formed ready to undergo still more complex changes, at the present day such matter would be instantly devoured or absorbed, which would not have been the case before living creatures were formed." In other words, bacteria and other organisms nearly everywhere present in our environment would immediately destroy any organic compound built up from simpler substances.

While Darwin doubted the usefulness of speculations about the origin of life, a few scientific thinkers proposed schemes of how life might have begun. Darwin's fiercest supporter, the English biologist Thomas Huxley, discussed how life might have arisen in the ocean. The biologist E. Pflüger, in 1875, proposed that life compounds might have arisen from the chemical cyanogen in the early stages of Earth's history.

One big problem with these discussions was that very little was known about the chemistry of living matter. As the British scientist J. D. Bernal writes in his book, *The Origin of Life:* "None of the nineteenth-century pioneers could really treat the question of origin they had so definitely raised, for at that time the essential chemical knowledge about the function of life did not exist. Biochemistry . . . which in the main is the language in which the problem of the origin of life has to be discussed, did not yet exist."

By 1924, the study of life compounds was somewhat more advanced, and in that year a young Russian biochemist, A. I. Oparin, published a booklet detailing some major ideas about the beginning of life. He argued that all life processes could be explained in terms of physical and chemical laws. Discussing the geological history of our planet, he proposed that the early atmosphere had been very unlike what it is today. It had many chemical substances such as ammonia, which combined into various active compounds. Rains washed these compounds into the ocean, where they continued to react with each other and the water. Various organic substances were formed in this way, Oparin hypothesized, including proteins. The protein molecules floating in the water met and combined with one another to form ever-larger and more complicated particles. He pointed out that such particles would tend to come out of solution and clump together to form jelly-like clots.

"The moment when the gel was precipitated or the first coagulum formed," Oparin wrote, "marked an extremely important stage in the process of the spontaneous generation of life. At this moment material which had formerly been structureless first acquired a structure and the transformation of organic compounds into an organic body took place. Not only this, but at the same time the body became an individual. Before this it had been inseparably fused with all the rest of the world, dissolved in it. Now, however, it separated itself out, though still very imperfectly, from that world and set itself apart from the environment surrounding it.

"With certain reservations we can even consider that first

piece of organic slime which came into being on the Earth as being the first organism. In fact it must have had many of those features which we now consider characteristics of life. It was composed of organic substances, it had a definite and complicated structure which was completely characteristic of it. It had a considerable store of chemical energy enabling it to undergo further transformations. Finally, even if it would not metabolize in the full sense of the word, it must certainly have had the ability to nourish itself, to absorb and assimilate substances from its environment, for this is present in every organic gel."

By this point in his arguments, Oparin had presented several major concepts: (1) The early atmosphere and waters of the earth were quite different in composition from today. (2) Organic molecules formed spontaneously from inorganic substances such as ammonia. (3) These organic molecules collected in self-contained units in the primitive oceans. Oparin went on to suggest a fourth important idea, that of chemical evolution, or prebiological evolution:

"It is hard to say precisely how the further development of this first organism went on, but still it is quite possible to establish the general direction of that development. Let us assume that in one of the corners of the earth, in the turbulent waves of the ocean, there were formed, either at the same time or one after the other, two bits of gel. Even if they separated out from the same solution they could not have been exactly alike. In one way or another they must have differed, for absolute identity does not exist on the Earth. Both bits were formed and floated in something that was not just water.

They were immersed, so to speak, in a nutrient mixture, in a solution, though a very weak one, of different substances, among which there were various organic compounds. And each of these bits of slime absorbed these substances from the medium which surrounded it. Each grew at the expense of these substances, but as each bit had a different structure from the other they assimilated the material from the environment at different rates, one faster, the other slower. The one with the physicochemical organization which made it possible to carry out the process of assimilation of hitherto foreign substances from the environment more quickly also grew faster than its weaker, less well-organized comrade. The more it grew and the larger its surface became the wider became this difference in the rate of growth."

Thus, the blob with the greater ability to grow would outstrip the other in size. Eventually, Oparin suggested, the gel would become so large that the action of waves or other mechanical forces would break it apart. Each piece would have much the same characteristics of the "parent." However, there would be slight individual variations, and again the organic particle or particles with the most efficient means of absorbing nutrients would grow the fastest, and reproduce more often.

Various chemical processes within the blob would tend to use up its available chemical energy, and only those gels would survive, Oparin said, that were able to gain energy from nutrients absorbed from the outside. Thus, the blobs gained the ability to "burn" chemical compounds absorbed from the environment, in order to produce energy.

Eventually, the supply of nutrient organic materials in the primeval ocean would become exhausted. This left two possibilities open to the gels. Either they could survive by preying on weaker comrades, or else they could develop means of nourishing themselves on very simple inorganic compounds. Some gels took the first path, and developed into the animals we know today, which feed on other organisms. Other bits of gel took the second course, and some of these developed the ability to photosynthesize food from sunlight, water, and air. By this time, the bits of gel could be considered to be living things.

Some of the specific facts and ideas in Oparin's paper have been disproven or else discarded as irrelevant. However, the major concepts he advanced have continued to dominate scientific thinking about the origin of life.

In 1929, a British scientist, J. B. Haldane, who did not know of Oparin's paper, published a short discussion on the same subject. He, too, suggested that Earth's early atmosphere had contained ammonia and other substances not now present. He proposed that there had been no free oxygen. Without oxygen, the atmosphere would have admitted larger amounts of ultraviolet light from the sun than it does now. The energetic ultraviolet light, acting on the substances in the atmosphere and ocean, would have created a "vast variety of organic substances . . . including sugars and apparently some of the materials from which proteins are built up." Haldane further suggested that these organic substances accumulated in the ocean until the primitive sea attained the consistency of "hot dilute soup." Haldane envisioned a process of chemical evolution somewhat akin to that proposed earlier by Oparin, leading eventually to cell life.

These two papers are the foundation stones of modern inquiry into the origin of life. Many papers published today on the subject still refer to Oparin and Haldane. It may be added that both these men maintained their interest in the subject and in 1963 met for the first time when they attended a conference on the origin of life held in Wakulla Springs, Florida.

7

HOW OLD IS LIFE ON OUR PLANET?

THE EARLY GREEKS seem to have been the first to recognize the significance of fossil remains found in many different kinds of sedimentary rocks—to realize that they represented various plants and animals that at one time inhabited our globe. The great Renaissance painter and scientist Leonardo da Vinci also suggested that the fossils of sea animals found in Italy indicated that the peninsula once had been under water. The full significance of fossils began to be recognized, however, only in the early nineteenth century, with the rise of the science of geology.

To create a fossil, an organism must usually first be buried. This most often takes place at the bottom of a body of water, usually the sea. The creature is covered with a layer of silt, mud, or sand. The sediment, in turn, is buried by added deposits and through pressure is turned into rock. Though much of the organism may decay, hard parts are often left behind. The most common fossils are bones, shells, and teeth, such as the shark teeth often found in piles of broken-up phosphate rock waiting to be made into fertilizer. A fossil may also consist of an impression left by an organism in soft mud that later is turned into rock. Such impressions are often left by plants which are too soft and fragile themselves to leave other fossil remains. Coal miners often discover prints of ferns impressed on the black rock they are extracting. Footprints of dinosaurs and other ancient animals have also been found in various parts of the world.

Much of the history of the continents appears to have consisted of times of uplift and mountain-building, followed by long periods of comparative geological quiet in which the forces of erosion gradually wore down the heights and deposited vast amounts of sediments. Most of the fossils we come across today were created during the times when sedimentation was active. The oldest fossils are laid down first, in the lowest layers of sediment, to be followed by younger fossils in sediments deposited atop the earlier layers.

The pioneer English geologist William Smith (1769–1839) observed that sedimentary rocks occur in various layers, or strata, one atop the other. He noted that each layer has its own characteristic types of fossils. Smith further saw that, in general, the lower the stratum, the more primitive are the fossils.

Thus, the position and the fossil content of a rock stratum

are clues about its geological age. The fossils gain an added importance if the rock layers have been seriously disturbed by crustal forces. Sometimes, foldings of the crust or other disturbances cause the strata to get out of sequence. By studying the fossils in the rocks, the geologist can determine what the original sequence of layers was, and perhaps gain an idea of what kind of rock shifts disturbed them.

The study of fossils also provides important clues about the kinds of organisms that flourished at a certain period, and the environment in which they lived.

By examining the rock strata over a wide area, geologists can reconstruct the history of the region. They have discovered that the histories of various parts of the Earth's surface dovetail, indicating that many events occurred on a worldwide scale. This is true of the major times of mountain-building and sedimentation.

Geologists divide Earth's history into broad divisions called eras. As we go back in time, life forms become simpler and more primitive. In the early part of the Paleozoic era, life was restricted to the seas and consisted of such creatures as jellyfish, corals, sea worms, shellfish, and seaweeds.

The first part of the Paleozoic era is known as the Cambrian period. The vast stretch of time before the Cambrian is often referred to as the Pre-Cambrian. Life arose sometime in the Pre-Cambrian.

So far we have discussed the geological past without mentioning any timetable. Until recently, geologists did not have any really accurate way to tell the ages of various rocks, and thus of fossils. By observing the present-day processes of erosion and sedimentation around them, they were able to estimate roughly how much time had been needed to lay down the rock strata of the past. But these guesses often were very inaccurate. In the 1930's, geologists began making use of a new technique called radioactive dating, or radiometric dating, based upon radioactive substances in the rocks. The greatest use of this method has come since 1950. Radiometric dating enables geologists to tell the ages of many different rocks with a high degree of accuracy.

Radiometric dating shows that the Cambrian period began about 600 million years ago. Since that time, life has progressed from the jellyfish and seaweed stage to organisms such as man and the flowering plants. Rocks laid down since the Pre-Cambrian have an abundance of fossils, and we can read the story of life's development with not too much trouble.

Many Pre-Cambrian rocks have been found on every continent. About one fifth of the surface rocks of the world are Pre-Cambrian, and Pre-Cambrian deposits are thought to underlie many surface rocks of more recent origin. Figure 7–1 shows the surface Pre-Cambrian rocks of the North American continent. Many of these North American surface Pre-Cambrian rocks are located in a great sheet known as the "Canadian shield." Other continents have similar shield areas. Most of the rest of the Pre-Cambrian rocks on the surface of the North American continent have been exposed as the result of erosion of younger deposits. This has taken place especially in mountain areas as rain and other erosion forces have stripped away the outer surfaces of peaks to reveal their Pre-Cambrian granite cores. In the southwestern part of the

7–1 The exposed Pre-Cambrian rocks of North America are shown in black on this map.

United States, the Colorado River has sliced thousands of feet deep through dozens of rock layers to expose Pre-Cambrian rock at the bottom of the Grand Canyon.

While more recent rocks are dated in millions of years, Pre-Cambrian rocks often stretch back billions of years into the past. (For British readers, it should be noted that we are using the term billion as it is used in the United States, to mean 1000 million, rather than 1 million million, as is the custom in the United Kingdom.) Pre-Cambrian rock ages of 2 billion years are not uncommon, and rocks dating back some 3.5

billion years have been found in Minnesota and the Soviet Union. Rocks of 3.5 billion years and greater have been located in South Africa and the Congo.

These rocks were formed from minerals derived from even older rocks that no longer exist. So the age of the Earth itself must be greater than 3.5 billion years. There is no way to estimate the age of the Earth directly from radiometric measurements of its rocks. However, astronomers believe that the meteorites which fall on our planet were formed at about the same time as the Earth and other planets. Radiometric dating shows that the meteorites are roughly 4.5 billion years old, so this is often taken as the age of the Earth.

7–2 Some of the steps in the development of life. The bottom time scale runs from 5 billion years ago to the present, which is marked zero.

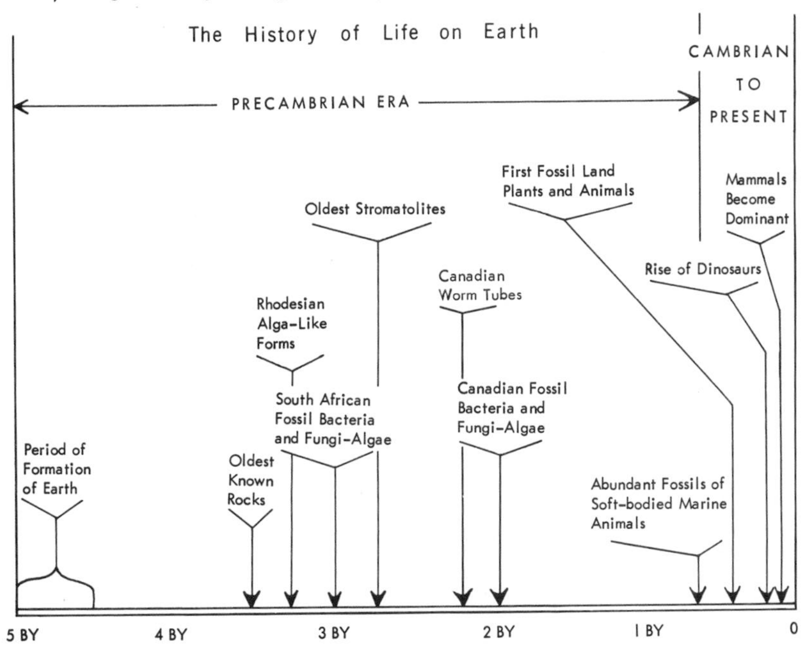

How long has life existed on our planet? In contrast with more recent rocks, Pre-Cambrian rocks contain few fossils. Fossils of jellyfish, sponges, and a few other types of simple animals have been found in late Pre-Cambrian sediments. Traces of algae are the only fossil remains of photosynthetic plants. All these organisms were marine forms, and no life is believed to have existed on land.

In spite of the scanty fossil records, scientists believe that Pre-Cambrian life, though simple, must have been abundant. Vast amounts of carbon are found in Pre-Cambrian deposits of graphite, and in black shales and slates. It is believed that at least some of this carbon is derived from the tissues of simple plants and animals buried in accumulating sediments.

The fossil record is sparse indeed in the older Pre-Cambrian rocks. Geologists have found evidence for algae. This evidence takes the form of rock structures called stromatolites, consisting of sheets, domes, and nodules of hardened sediments (Figures 7–3 and 7–4). Stromatolites are still being formed today by colonies of algae living in shallow sea waters. It is thought that stromatolites found in Pre-Cambrian rocks were also formed by colonies of these simple green plants. Stromatolites have been found in rocks as old as 2.7 billion years. By studying these structures, formed in shallow Pre-Cambrian waters, scientists can sometimes learn about the heights of ocean tides in that remote age. In 1968, the American geologist Paul Hoffman reported finding tube structures in Canadian sedimentary rocks about 2.2 billion years old. He believes the tubes were the borrows of marine worms.

In the 1950's, scientists discovered that certain fine-grained

7–3 Canadian Pre-Cambrian stromatolites which occur in limestone between 1.8 and 2.5 billion years old. The hammer gives the scale. Like the recently formed stromatolites shown in Figure 7–4, these structures are believed to have been formed by mats of blue-green algae trapping grains of calcium carbonate sediment.

7–4 Recent stromatolites located in the intertidal zone along a part of the Australian coast. These are less than 2000 years old. The top photo shows stromatolites in place. They average about a yard across. The bottom photo shows several structures removed from their rock base.

Pre-Cambrian sediments had trapped and preserved various microscopic organisms (Figures 7–5, 7–6, and 7–7).

In 1953, the late Samuel Tyler, a geologist at the University of Wisconsin, discovered a variety of microfossils in black chert (flint) found in an area known as the Gunflint Iron Formation that is part of the lower edge of the Canadian shield. The area is in Ontario, on the northern edge of Lake Superior. The black color of the chert is believed to come from organic material. The age of the chert, based on radiometric dating, is around 1.9 billion years.

During the next ten years, Tyler studied the microfossils in collaboration with Elso Barghoorn, a biologist at Harvard University who specializes in the study of ancient life. First, samples of the chert were prepared for microscopic examination by grinding and polishing them into very thin plates, or sections. Each section was much thinner than a sheet of paper, so thin that it was transparent.

Hundreds of sections were prepared and studied under the

7–5 Filaments from the Gunflint chert as revealed under the electron microscope. These are thought to be the remains of photosynthetic algae.

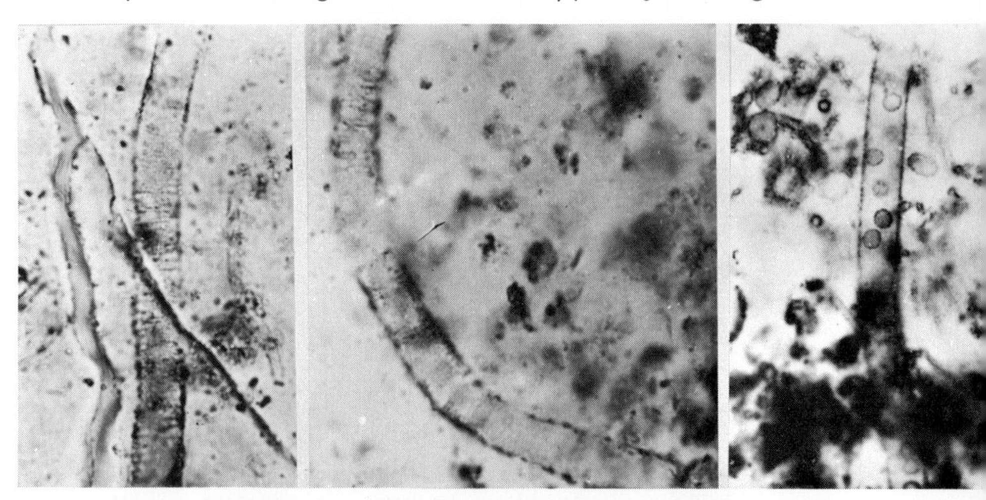

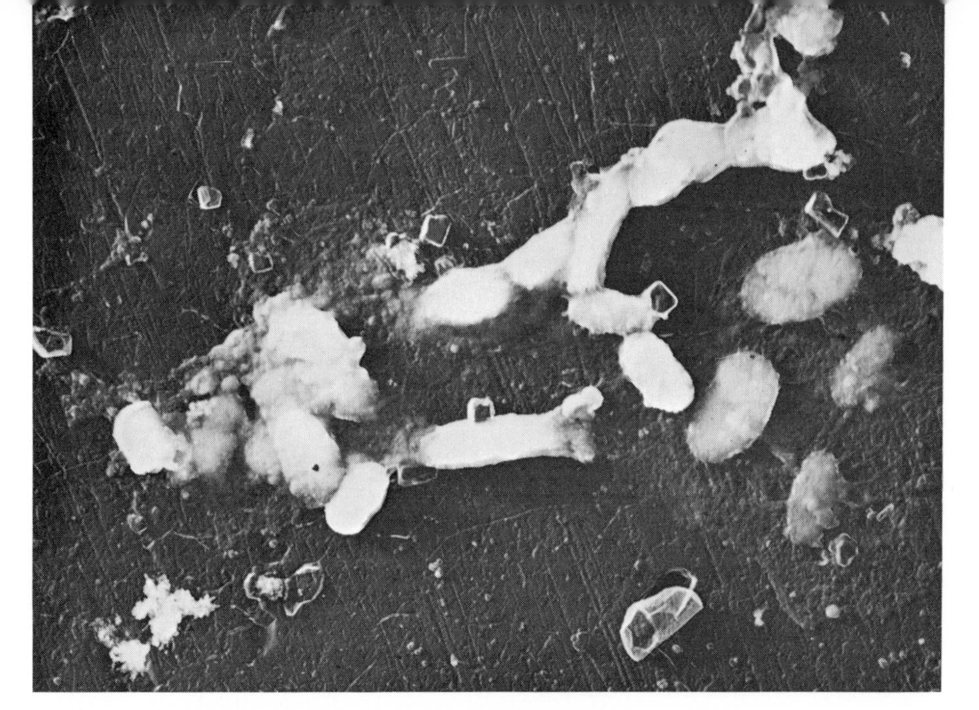

7–6 Bacterial rod shapes from the Gunflint cherts. Some of the bacteria are isolated, while others are arranged in a filament.

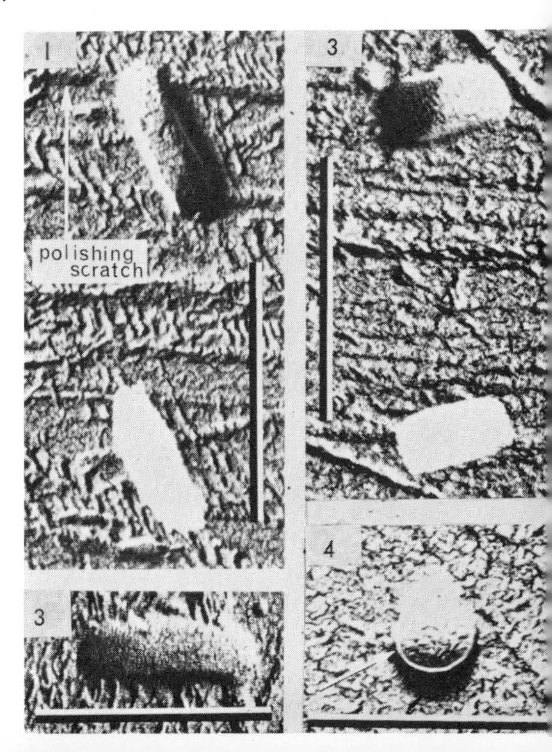

7–7 Bacterial shapes from Pre-Cambrian rocks in South Africa that are slightly more than 3 billion years old. The bars represent one micron, or 1/1000 millimeter. Photo 4 shows a cross section of a bacterium and apparently the remains of the cell wall.

light microscope. The microscope revealed a variety of well-preserved microorganisms. The most common fossils were filaments and patterned round spheres very similar to the forms of modern algae or fungi. The algae grew in sheets or mats in shallow waters. Also found in the chert were rod-shaped and spherical single-celled bacteria. Both types of bacteria closely resemble iron-depositing bacteria living today.

The report of these investigations, published in February 1965, aroused great scientific interest, for the microorganisms were the oldest fossils to be discovered up to that time. That same month, however, Barghoorn was in the eastern Transvaal region of South Africa, collecting samples of black chert slightly more than 3 billion years old. The samples were collected from an outcrop exposed by a road cut near the entrance of a gold mine.

When thin sections were examined under the light microscope, small bodies were visible but not clearly. Barghoorn and a co-investigator, J. William Schopf, turned to the electron microscope, which revealed rod-shaped cells and patterned spherical shapes. The rod shapes resemble modern bacteria. In some cases, the team obtained cross sections of the microorganisms and were able to observe cell walls.

The patterned spherical shapes may have been single-celled algae. If true, that would indicate that photosynthetic organisms existed as much as 3 billion years ago.

The results of the research were published in 1966 and 1967. The investigators concluded that the finding of bacteria and, possibly, algae in the South African chert indicates that life arose in the first 30 per cent of Earth's history—sometime between 3 billion and 4.5 billion years ago.

In 1968, a new report by Barghoorn and two collaborators was published. This told of a chemical analysis that was done on various Pre-Cambrian black cherts, ranging in age from 1 to more than 3 billion years. The analysis was aimed at finding out what amino acids (the building blocks of proteins) may have been present in the ancient organisms.

Great care had to be taken to make sure that no amino acids were introduced into the samples from the environment. The equipment was cleaned with acid solution and the chemicals used in the tests were checked to make sure that they contained no amino acid contamination. The researchers wore fresh plastic gloves throughout the tests to avoid introducing amino acids from their skin or perspiration. Each sample of chert, about the size of a hand, was thoroughly washed and then immersed in acid solution overnight to remove all possible contaminants. The samples then were powdered and the chemical tests were made on the powder.

In all of the cherts, the researchers found traces of amino acids. What is more, these amino acids were present in about the same proportions as they are in organisms living today. This suggests that the chemical make-up of the earliest single-celled organisms differed little from that of modern living things.

This brings us to the question of how the first cells arose. The answer to this depends partly on our knowledge of conditions on the early Earth. That is the subject of the next chapter.

8

THE EARLY EARTH

HOW DID THE Earth originate? A number of answers have been proposed by scientists through the years. During the first half of our century, the most popular theories were those that conceived of the Earth and other planets being born out of a filament of hot gas ejected from the sun, either as a result of some kind of internal solar explosion or the gravitational attraction of a passing star. The Earth, according to this viewpoint, condensed from an eddy or ball of hot gas. It first was molten and then gradually formed a crust as it cooled. Some of the substances in the original cloud remained gaseous at ordinary Earth temperatures, and these formed our first atmosphere.

An alternative hypothesis was that the creation of the planets was a by-product of the forming of the sun. This viewpoint dates back hundreds of years. During the last few

Thompson, Paul D. LC 78-82399

ABIOGENESIS: From Molecule to Cell *Ages 12 up Grades 7 up*

Introducing Modern Science

Illustrated by Mary Lybarger

192 pp. **6 x 8** **$4.95** **677**

Abiogenesis is the science of the origin of living organisms from lifeless matter, and deals with how life arose. This book presents some of the biochemical discoveries about the processes of life and the impetus that gave rise to the first molecules and cells. The author also speculates about life on the other planets and the solar system.

September 1969

CAN BE RELATED TO: Science.

PAUL D. THOMPSON has also written *Gases and Plasmas* and *The Virus Realm.*

decades modern versions of it have become widely accepted by astronomers and geologists.

Astronomers have found that vast amounts of cold gases and dust exist in our galaxy. Clouds of these materials are visible through the telescope. Astronomers believe that new stars are continually being born in such clouds. They think our own solar system condensed from an eddy of gas and dust some 5 billion years ago (Figure 8–1). The scientists visualize that a local region of swirling cloud slowly became more dense as gravitation and other forces drew the particles closer together. Eventually, a great spinning disk of dust and gases was formed. The material in the center of the disk contracted

8–1 *An artist's conception of the formation of the Earth.*

into a ball that became the sun. Various eddies existed in the disk. Grains of dust in each eddy frequently collided with each other and stuck together, as such particles do in the vacuum of space. In this way, larger and larger particles were formed. These in turn collided and produced larger bodies. Eventually, in each eddy, one body grew large enough to capture others by gravitational attraction. Thus, "protoplanets" arose.

By studying the light of stars, astronomers are able to tell what elements are found in them, and in what proportion. For example, stars such as our sun are made up largely of hydrogen and helium, with small percentages of other elements in gaseous form. From these observations, astronomers have constructed tables showing the abundance of various elements in the universe. When we compare these cosmic abundances with the abundance of the same elements on Earth, some interesting discrepancies occur that help us learn about conditions on the primitive Earth.

Does our present atmosphere date back to the beginnings of Earth? Study of the abundances of the elements argon, neon, krypton, and xenon help us to answer this question. These gaseous elements are very inert, or chemically lazy. They are almost never found in chemical combination with atoms of other elements. Thus, in the primeval cloud from which Earth was formed, these inert elements would not have been bound chemically to other substances but would have existed as free gases. If the early Earth had an atmosphere, the gases in it included a certain percentage of argon, neon, krypton, and xenon. However, although our present atmosphere does contain traces of these inert gases, they are much less abundant than we would expect from their cosmic abundance. We can infer from this that the gases in the primeval cosmic eddy dissipated as the Earth was accumulating from rocks and dust, or else that the Earth's first atmosphere was lost sometime after the formation of the planet. This might have been caused by the planet's heating up to the point where the first atmosphere "boiled off" into space.

We would expect at least some heating to take place during and after the formation of Earth. Part of the heating would come from the impact of dust particles and stones on the surface of the planet, as the Earth attracted these materials from the space around it. Some heating would occur from the compression of materials by gravity as the planet grew larger. And there would be some heating from radioactive materials in the Earth's crust. A fourth source of heat would be the tidal movements of Earth's crust due to the rotation of the planet and the gravitational tug of the sun and moon.

We know that enough heat was generated to melt much of the interior of the planet. Heavier materials tended to sink down toward the center of the Earth, and thus our planet gained its iron-nickel core. Lighter materials, such as silica, tended to rise, and now make up the greater part of the Earth's outer layer. It could be that the globe became so hot that large areas of its outer surface melted. In that case, any primitive atmosphere might have been driven off by the heat.

Whether or not general melting took place, we can assume from geological evidence that there was considerable volcanic activity during the Pre-Cambrian portion of Earth's history.

A volcano occurs when cracking of the crust releases some of the pressure on the underlying rock. This rock is very hot, but ordinarily the pressure of overlying layers prevents it from melting. Once the pressure is relieved somewhat, the rock melts and a pool of magma forms. This magma is still under pressure and it seeks to find a way out of its confined space, creeping upward through cracks in the crust. When the Earth was formed originally, large amounts of gases were trapped in the rocks, often in chemical combination with other substances. When subterranean rock melts, these gases are dissolved in the magma, and as the magma creeps upward toward the Earth's surface and reaches zones of lower pressure, the gases tend to come out of solution, much as bubbles of carbon dioxide come out of solution when a bottle of carbonated pop is opened. The gases include water vapor, carbon dioxide, hydrogen sulfide, hydrogen chloride, and nitrogen. Much of the gas in magma is released to the atmosphere when the molten rock reaches the surface as lava (Figure 8–2).

There are about 500 active volcanoes on Earth today. We know from ancient lava fields and other evidence that vulcanism has been at work through the planet's geological history. It has been suggested that volcanoes were even more numerous back in Pre-Cambrian times.

Many scientists believe that much of Earth's early atmosphere came from the gases released by volcanoes. Volcanoes do not emit free oxygen, and there are many reasons to believe that free oxygen was not an important part of the atmosphere through much or most of Pre-Cambrian times. Some of this evidence comes from geochemical studies of early sedimentary rocks. Sedimentary rocks are formed from debris of older

8–2 *Geologists collecting gases released by a Hawaiian volcano.*

rocks that have been disintegrated by weathering. There are two kinds of weathering that work together to attack rocks. In mechanical weathering, heat, cold, and frost break rock apart into smaller fragments. In chemical weathering, water and air attack substances in the rock. Oxygen is important in chemical weathering. It attacks metal-containing minerals in the rock. For example, when it comes in contact with iron-rich minerals, oxygen combines with the iron to form rust. The presence of water speeds this reaction. Water also aids weathering in another way. When the mineral is oxidized, it forms soluble compounds which soon are dissolved and carried away by the water.

One major rock ingredient is not affected by chemical weathering. This is quartz, which is a compound of silica and oxygen. Because it already is oxidized, quartz is not attacked by the atmosphere and it is insoluble in water. So, when a rock weathers, its newly oxidized compounds are dissolved and carried away in water, leaving the quartz, which is slowly broken up by mechanical weathering into pebbles, gravel, and sand.

The ingredients of the rock are transported by running water into lowland areas or into the ocean, where they are deposited. The quartz fragments are deposited according to weight; the heavier ones drop to the bottom first, while the lighter ones are carried farther out to sea before settling out. Thus, a bed of quartz sand will usually contain grains of much the same size. The oxidized minerals dissolved in the water are not deposited with the sand; they are carried onward. Eventually, these dissolved minerals combine with each other and precipitate out of solution, to form deposits of clay. Thus, due to the presence of oxygen in our atmosphere, we find that there is a separation of sedimentary materials: quartz sands are deposited by themselves, while the other elements of the rock are deposited as clays in other locations. Under present-day conditions, therefore, we do not ordinarily find mixed deposits of quartz grains and grains of metal-containing minerals. In an atmosphere without free oxygen, however, the situation would be different. There would be no oxygen to attack nonquartz minerals and make them soluble in water. These minerals thus would not chemically weather very rapidly but instead would be subjected to much the same kind of mechanical weathering that quartz undergoes. Pebbles, gravel, and sands made up of both quartz and other minerals would be created. These would be deposited by water according to weight of the particles, rather than their composition. We would expect to find sands made up not only of quartz but of other mineral grains.

In 1958, the geologist P. Ramdohr published a study of very

old Pre-Cambrian rocks formed from sands and gravels. The rock samples he studied came from the shield areas of Africa, South America, and North America. In addition to quartz grains, these ancient deposits contain a number of other mineral particles, such as iron and sulfur and uranium compounds. Such particles, many geologists believe, would not have been present if the ancient sediments had been created and deposited under an atmosphere containing free oxygen.

There are other arguments for the lack of free oxygen in the early atmosphere of Earth. It has been found that free oxygen acts as a "poison" to destroy many compounds that are vital to life. These compounds today exist only in living cells, where they are protected from the atmosphere. If cells arose in Pre-Cambrian times from various compounds created by inorganic processes, the absence of free oxygen was essential to the creation and preservation of these compounds.

How long ago did the atmosphere of Earth form? Sediments dated as 3.2 billion years old have been found in South Africa. These could not have been created without the weathering effects of an atmosphere. Nor could they have been deposited without substantial quantities of water. Thus, as early as 3.2 billion years ago the Earth must have had air and bodies of water, perhaps oceans.

What a desolate picture the Pre-Cambrian scene must have made! Mountains and lowlands bare of any trace of life. No dark loamy soils as we know them, rich in humus and other organic matter; only water-laid deposits of various-colored sands and gravels. Seas equally lifeless. The sole life of the landscape comes from the ceaseless activity of volcanoes and the elements: the volcanoes spewing forth lava and steam and gases; periodic rainstorms beating against the bare rocks of the mountains; and rushing streams carrying away bits of material to the lowlands and seas.

The atmosphere would have been unfit to support human life, because it lacked oxygen and also because it contained gases poisonous to today's air-breathing creatures. Any human explorer in that bleak landscape would not only have had to use a breathing apparatus but would have had to wear special clothing to protect him from the fierce rays of the sun. For oxygen in our atmosphere shields us from much of the ultraviolet radiation of the sun—even the small amount that gets through is enough to give a person a bad sunburn in a few hours on a summer's day. In an atmosphere without oxygen, the UV rays would have been so intense as to kill living organisms exposed to the direct sunlight.

It seems contradictory to imagine life's arising in a place so hostile to life. However, the early Pre-Cambrian environment provided the key ingredients for the creation of life: simple carbon compounds from volcanic exhalations, plus the energy needed to rip them apart and link them together to form more complex molecules, the molecules of life. This energy was available from the intense ultraviolet light of the sun, from storm lightning, from the heat of volcanoes and recently erupted lava, and from incandescently hot meteorites plunging through the atmosphere. True, the first living things could not survive on the sun-blasted surface of the land, but could in the seas or lakes, where the water would filter out ultraviolet light, or in the shaded crevices of the Pre-Cambrian soil and rocks.

Geologists are investigating what compounds would be present in the early atmosphere and oceans to serve as the building blocks for more complex molecules. This question, of course, is of great interest to biochemists trying to figure out how life first arose.

Nitrogen, and a number of simple carbon, hydrogen, and oxygen compounds, would be present in volcanic gases. Those are the four main elements of life. Some elements and compounds would be released by weathering of rocks; these would include many of the metals and their compounds. Thus, we would have a three-phase system, with the solid land contributing substances to the ocean and air, the sea contributing water vapor and certain other gases to the atmosphere, and the air rich in various gases that, upon combining into more complex compounds, would be washed by the rain into the soil and the ocean.

In the early 1950's, the noted American chemist Harold Urey and his associates argued that methane (CH_4), ammonia (NH_3), water vapor, and hydrogen were probably important ingredients of the early atmosphere. As a result, many of the major experiments in the artificial creation of life compounds have made use of mixtures of these gases. However, other researchers, led by Philip Abelson, have put forth equally persuasive arguments that the early atmosphere contained mainly carbon dioxide, carbon monoxide, hydrogen, and water vapor. Further research may in time help scientists to decide between the two hypotheses, or to reconcile them in a grand synthesis.

9

CREATING LIFE COMPOUNDS IN THE LABORATORY

After Urey hypothesized that methane and ammonia were important ingredients of the Earth's early atmsophere, he suggested an experiment to a graduate student of his at the University of Chicago. The student, Stanley Miller, built an apparatus like the one shown in Figure 9–1. The lower part of the apparatus contained water, while the air in the upper sections was replaced with a mixture of methane, ammonia, and hydrogen gases. Heat was applied to the lower flask to boil the water. The water vapor rose and circulated around the circuit of the tubing, mixing with the other gases. In a chamber below the large upper flask, a pair of electrodes provided energy in the form of a continuous electrical discharge across the gap between the electrodes. The gases circulated past this

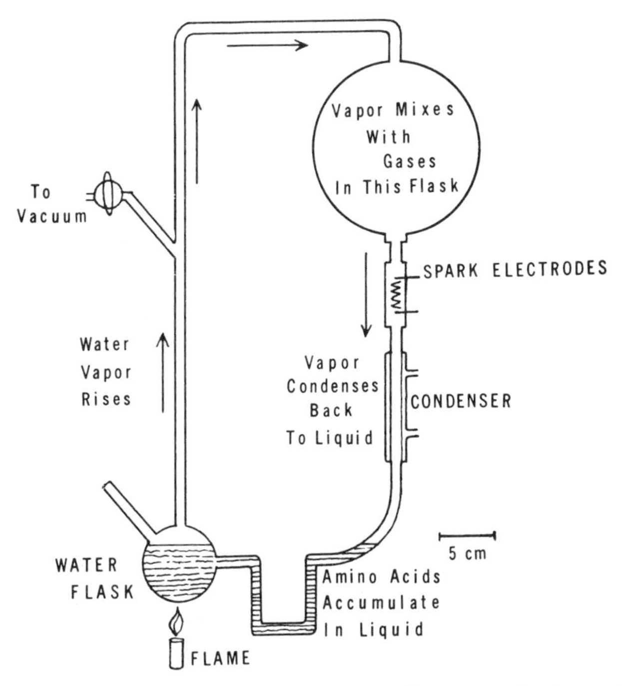

9–1 *The apparatus used by Stanley Miller to synthesize amino acids.*

discharge into a cold condenser section. The water vapor condensed into droplets, which ran down into the lower section of the apparatus to mix with the water there.

Miller expected that any compounds created by the electric discharge would be removed from the gases by the condensation of the water, and that the compounds would accumulate in the lower section of the apparatus.

Because the apparatus was closed, the water in it circulated continuously, first evaporating and passing past the discharge, then condensing and running back into the lower section of the equipment, only to be evaporated again. Miller ran the apparatus for a week without a halt. In May 1953, he reported what happened in an issue of the magazine *Science*.

"During the run," he wrote in his report, "the water in the flask became noticeably pink after the first day, and by the end of the week the solution was deep red and turbid." At the end of the week, the liquid was removed for analysis (Figure 9–2). The turbidity, or cloudiness, of the solution proved to be due to silica eroded from the glass of the apparatus. The red color was from organic compounds. Further analysis showed that among these compounds were several types of amino acids, including glycine and alanine. As the reader will recall, such amino acids are building blocks of proteins, the key molecules of life.

9–2 *A graph showing the results of the Miller experiment.*

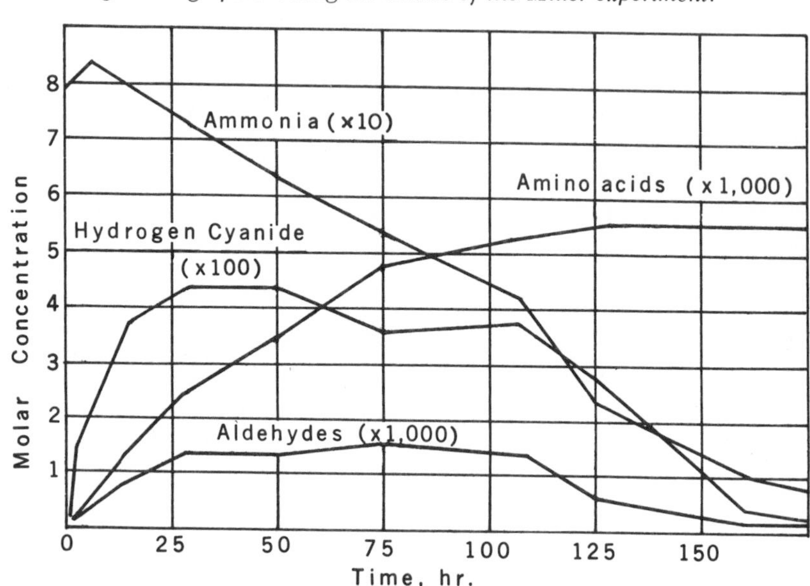

Miller's experiment helped to show that some of the building blocks of life could have been created by inorganic processes from gases possibly present in the early atmosphere of Earth. The report of the experiment triggered similar investigations in a number of other laboratories around the world. Some experimenters concentrated on enlarging Miller's results by varying the sources of energy or the starting ingredients. Several researchers, among them the German scientist W. Groth, were able to synthesize amino acids from water, methane, and ammonia by using ultraviolet light. Others used atomic radiation, while still others used heat. Philip Abelson, who has vigorously opposed the idea that methane and ammonia were important ingredients of Earth's early atmosphere, showed that various mixtures of carbon dioxide, carbon monoxide, water, nitrogen, and hydrogen yielded amino acids when subjected to electrical discharges. Thus, it appears that any of the mixtures of gases proposed for the early atmosphere would have produced amino acids, as long as adequate sources of energy were available.

Such experiments have given a tremendous impetus to the study of the question of the origin of life. For the laboratory findings have helped to give concrete proof that, under the proper conditions, compounds believed to be characteristic of life can arise without life. One sign of the growing interest in the field of life's origins is the various conferences that have been held on the subject since Miller's first experiments. In 1956, the New York Academy of Sciences and the American Association for the Advancement of Science held a symposium on "Modern Views of Spontaneous Generation." The following year, the first international conference on "The Origin of Life on Earth" was held in Moscow. In 1958, a symposium on "Biochemical Origins" was held by the American Chemical Society at a San Francisco meeting. In 1963, the second international conference on the origin of life was held at Wakulla Springs, Florida. Another sign of interest in the subject is the willingness of the United States government to help subsidize some of the research, in connection with its program of exploring for life on other bodies of the solar system.

In living organisms, amino acids are linked together into chains with the aid of enzymes according to "instructions" from DNA. On the primitive Earth, how could amino acid chains have been formed to create the first proteins? Linking together amino acids into peptide chains requires energy, either from a direct source or from the presence of other chemical compounds. A number of researchers have carried out experiments in this area, and have found that it is indeed possible to create peptide chains by inorganic processes which may have been present on the primitive Earth. For example, when a water solution of glycine and leucine (two amino acids) is exposed to ultraviolet light in the presence of cyanamide, amino acid pairs are formed. A mechanism such as this might have helped create peptide chains on the primordial Earth. Another mechanism that has aroused great interest is being explored by Sidney Fox and his associates at the University of Miami in Florida. They have shown that amino acids can be formed by passing methane, ammonia, and water through a silica tube heated to 900–1000° Celsius (Centigrade). The silica acts as a catalyst to promote creation of the amino acids. Silica is the main ingredient of quartz, which is the second most abundant mineral on Earth. Fox also has found that heating dry amino acids yields peptide chains incorporating more than 100 units. Fox calls these peptide chains "proteinoids," and he suggests that natural heat sources on the primeval Earth could both have formed amino acids and then linked those units into the first proteins. More will be said about Fox's proteinoids shortly.

One intermediate compound formed when a primitive atmosphere, either of the Urey or Abelson model, is energized is hydrogen cyanide. In 1966, two scientists working for an American chemical firm reported another possible pathway by which proteins could be formed. Clifford Matthews and Robert E. Moser found that hydrogen cyanide molecules, when supplied with energy, can link together to form chains. When these long molecules are immersed in water, further spontaneous chemical reactions take place to convert the molecular links into amino acids; in other words, the chains become converted into peptide chains. The two scientists suggested that hydrogen cyanide chains could have been formed in the primitive atmosphere. Upon settling into the ocean, the chains would have been converted rapidly into proteins.

Thus, we see that proteins could have been formed by a variety of chemical pathways on the early Earth. In the new perspective offered by laboratory research, it now appears that protein formation was a commonplace event some billions of years ago. In fact, it would have been remarkable if proteins had *not* been formed.

Another major large molecule essential to life today is

nucleic acid. The reader will recall that DNA and RNA are formed from subunits called nucleotides. Each nucleotide consists of three parts: a base group, a sugar molecule, and a phosphate group. A number of experiments have been carried out to find ways that nucleotides could have been created abiogenetically and then linked into nucleic acids. Among the most interesting of these experiments are some carried out by Cyril Ponnamperuma and his associates at the National Aeronautics and Space Administration's laboratory in California (Figure 9–3). From intermediate compounds believed present in the early atmosphere, such as hydrogen cyanide and formaldehyde, they have synthesized a variety of organic

9–3 *The scientist Cyril Ponnamperuma and a sparkling apparatus for creating organic compounds from simple chemicals.*

compounds, including some bases and sugars. When the bases and sugars are mixed in a solution of hydrogen cyanide, the substance acts as a catalyst to link bases to sugars to form what are called nucleosides. A nucleoside is a nucleotide minus the phosphate group. Another researcher, the German scientist Gerhard Schramm, finds that after mixing certain nucleosides with phosphorus-containing compounds, the nucleosides not only gain the needed phosphate groups but spontaneously link together to form primitive nucleic acids. While the phosphorus compounds he used were laboratory chemicals, there easily may have been somewhat similar compounds on the Earth in the first days.

Another class of giant molecules is the carbohydrates, the long sugar and starch chains formed from simple sugars. Simple sugars such as glucose, scientists find, can be synthesized from the primitive intermediate compound formaldehyde, and the sugars in turn can be linked into chains fairly easily.

Still another class of key molecules is the lipids. In 1960, W. T. Wilson, of Victoria University in New Zealand, reported that he had synthesized lipid molecules from a solution of ammonia and certain other substances energized by electric discharges. The lipid material formed a layer on the surface of the liquid. Since most experimenters are concerned largely with proteins and nucleic acids, not a great deal of further research has been done in synthesizing lipids.

Earlier we mentioned that the compound ATP serves as an energy transfer unit between the processes of food breakdown and molecule building. When food is broken down, phosphate groups are added to ADP molecules to transform them to ATP.

The energy stored in the bond holding the phosphate group is released by the removal of the group, and can be used in construction of molecules. ATP thus is a "storage battery" molecule for conserving energy.

Ponnamperuma and his associates have been able to synthesize ATP from the base adenine and the sugar ribose by mixing them with a phosphorus-containing compound and exposing the mixture to ultraviolet light.

It must be stressed that these laboratory experiments simply show us *possible* routes by which major life compounds may have been synthesized naturally on the early Earth. We have no way of knowing at the present time exactly what reactions *actually* took place some 4 billion years ago. In the words of J. Oro, of the University of Houston in Texas, a major figure in this area of research: "There are more questions to be asked than answers to be given on the subject of stages and mechanisms of prebiological organic synthesis."

What scientists hope is that when enough data are gathered, one or more series of chemical reactions will appear as the obvious and logical pathways by which life arose from simple substances. It may be that all the steps will never be discovered, or perhaps several alternative possible pathways will present themselves and researchers will be unable to choose which one was actually taken.

Meanwhile, a new vocabulary is emerging to describe the processes which scientists are investigating. The old term "spontaneous generation" has largely been abandoned because of the historical associations connected with it. In its place, many scientists are using the term "biopoesis," or "life-making," coined by the English scientist N. W. Pirie. Some use is also made of another term invented by Pirie: "eobiont," meaning the first living organism to arise as a result of biopoesis. Some researchers use the word "biogenesis" when speaking of the rise of life, but this is not strictly correct, since the word traditionally has been used for the doctrine that all life comes from life. Others more correctly use the term "abiogenesis." Since "organic" can refer either to materials formed by living creatures or to substances formed by other processes, many scientists prefer to speak of "biogenetic" compounds (those formed by living things) and "abiogenetic" compounds (those created without the aid of living things). Another common term is "prebiological," used to refer to the time in Earth's history before the rise of life; the phrase "prebiological systems" is often used to refer to organized assemblages of molecules that might have preceded the first living creature.

The laboratory experiments conducted so far have shown that it is possible to synthesize building blocks such as amino acids under possible primitive Earth conditions, and to join those building blocks to form larger molecules such as Fox's proteinoids. However, there is still a tremendously wide gap between such molecules and a living cell. For example, one characteristic of life is its ability to reproduce itself in substantially the same form from generation to generation. We do not yet have any clear idea of how such a self-reproducing system could arise abiogenetically. As the scientist Peter Mora has pointed out, the laboratory experiments have shown how the *materials* of life may have been formed, but they do not demonstrate how *living processes* arose. He has even questioned whether or not the present laws of chemistry and physics are sufficient to explain the origin of life. There may be as yet unknown principles governing the creation and existence of living creatures, Mora believes.

As opposed to Mora's pessimism, a number of other scientists believe that we have a good chance of success in unraveling and understanding the mystery of life's origin. And Bernal has added the thought that once we understand how life arose, it should not be too difficult to create it in the laboratory.

10

FROM MOLECULES TO CELLS

WHILE ULTRAVIOLET LIGHT may have provided the energy for the synthesis of important compounds on the early Earth, this same energy could be very destructive to larger molecules and life processes. Dr. Carl Sagon of Harvard University has calculated that, in the absence of free atmospheric oxygen, the ultraviolet light falling on Earth's surface was intense enough to kill many modern organisms in a few seconds. Escape from this deluge of high-energy light was possible, Sagon points out, several dozen yards down in the ocean, for the water would filter out much of the radiation. Thus, bodies of water might be the logical place for the first cells to arise. On the other hand, it probably would have been unlikely for life to arise in the deeper waters of the ocean, for there would be a complete absence of any light, visible or ultraviolet, and a corresponding lack of energy to help boost chemical compounds into higher states of organization. So the shallow water near a coast or in an inland sea would appear to be the best possible place for life to arise. Other possible locations might be lakes or pools. Some scientists have suggested that volcanic hot springs might be good places, for the higher water temperatures might promote faster chemical reactions, and such springs also might be especially rich in dissolved minerals useful to the first eobionts.

A few scientists have argued that life arose not in bodies of water but on the land. They suggest that the first living organisms could have arisen in the shaded crevices between soil or gravel particles. Perhaps the sea was colonized by life forms from the land.

Life indeed could have arisen in several different environments. The early Earth, with its oceans and pools, volcanoes and sediments, must have presented a wide variety of natural chemical laboratories in which life could perhaps have arisen not once but several times, under a number of conditions.

Even among scientists who agree that life arose in shallow waters, there is considerable difference of opinion as to the circumstances under which it sprang into being. Many scientists feel that one of the first steps had to be some concentration of the simple substances making up the thin organic "soup." They believe that this concentration was necessary to promote chemical reactions among the various molecules. Different mechanisms for concentrating the substances have been suggested. J. D. Bernal points out that the surfaces of minerals have the ability to hold various molecules and even to promote chemical reactions between them. He proposes that mudbanks deposited by rivers in shallow coastal waters served as surfaces on which abiogenetically formed organic molecules became concentrated. Other scientists have proposed that the concentration took place inside or on the surfaces of free-floating particles, such as protein blobs.

Some scientists, however, think that the conditions necessary for forming large molecules and having them interact would be best achieved in a dilute watery environment.

If we assume that life arose in the sea, we visualize a dilute mixture of many different abiogenetically formed molecules, including amino acids and simple proteins, nucleotides and primitive nucleic acid molecules, sugars, and perhaps lipid molecules of various kinds. There also were many inorganic elements and compounds, such as sodium, chlorine, copper, iron, phosphorus compounds, etc.

The central mystery of the origin of life right now is how these diverse elements came into relationships with each other and achieved the characteristics of life as we know it. Those characteristics include:

1. Cellular form.
2. Use of enzyme catalysts to break down food molecules to obtain energy and to build up needed organic molecules.
3. Direction of cell activities by means of enzymes produced according to information contained in nucleic acid molecules.
4. Reproduction of nucleic acid molecules.
5. Reproduction of the entire cell by fissioning.

We cannot tell in what order these characteristics arose. Some of them may have occurred, to use a favorite term of Bernal's, *pari passu*—that is, simultaneously and at an equal rate of progress.

Bernal is intrigued by the ability of mineral grains to hold various molecules on their surfaces and to promote reactions between them. He suggests that life arose on and in mudbanks deposited in shallow ocean waters at the mouths of rivers. A primitive metabolism of breaking down and building up compounds could arise among the molecules on the surfaces of the mineral grains, a situation he has compared to a "cold flame." Here also could occur the chemical reactions needed to produce the first protein enzymes and self-duplicating nucleic acids. He sees these "sub-vital areas" of mud developing an interlocking set of chemical reactions that might be considered life. Only later, with the development of appropriate membranes, Bernal suggests, would separate organisms arise.

This hypothesis has not found favor with many of the scientists investigating the origin of life. Most think that one of the earliest steps must have been the creation of cell-like particles that could incorporate many different molecules and eventually develop life.

In the forefront of these investigators has been the pioneer researcher A. I. Oparin. In his 1924 booklet on the nature of life, he proposed that protein blobs played a key role in the development of cellular life. He pointed out that proteins and other large molecules form unstable solutions when dissolved in water. Given slight changes in the solution (such as a change in the acidity or alkalinity), the molecules tend to come out of solution and cling together. He postulated that protein blobs or gels could have originated in this manner to form the first primitive "cells."

The formation of such gels was investigated by H. B. Bungenberg de Jong and his associates. They found that in a protein solution, droplets of semiliquid consistency would spontaneously appear. Oparin and his fellow workers have spent much of their time investigating these "coacervates" and how they might have given rise to the first cells.

In one experiment, Oparin made a solution containing molecules of the nucleotide adenine and also molecules of the protein histone. He used an enzyme to promote linking of the adenine molecules into nucleic acid molecules. When this process took place in the presence of histone, coacervates formed incorporating both the protein and the newly formed nucleic acid. Oparin argues that during the time that proteins and nucleic acids were being synthesized in the primeval ocean, they would have become associated in such coacervates.

Other experiments by Oparin and his associates show that coacervates can take up substances from their environment and concentrate them. For example, if the dye methylene blue is introduced into the external solution, the coacervates absorb and concentrate the dye molecules. This also happens with other substances, such as amino acids.

Besides absorbing various materials, coacervates can also release substances. In addition, certain chemical reactions can take place in coacervates, sometimes more rapidly than in the surrounding medium. In one experiment, coacervate drops were prepared containing an enzyme that links glucose molecules together to form starch. These drops were placed in a solution of glucose. Each coacervate absorbed glucose and transformed it into a growing store of insoluble starch inside the drop. In another experiment, droplets were prepared containing not only the original enzyme but an enzyme that chops starch molecules into maltose sugar fragments. When placed in a glucose solution, the coacervates absorbed glucose molecules, converted them into starch, and then transformed the starch into maltose. As this process went on, the maltose was "excreted" to the medium. So each droplet absorbed glucose and gave out maltose. When a drop contained more of enzyme Number 1 than of Number 2, starch was made faster than it could be changed to maltose. As the starch accumulated, the droplet grew in size. When a droplet contained more of enzyme Number 2, however, it shrank and eventually disappeared.

Another experiment consisted of having droplets containing an enzyme that links nucleosides together to form nucleic acid chains. Adenine nucleosides were dissolved in the surrounding medium. As a result, a number of nucleic acid chains were formed inside the coacervate.

Oparin visualizes a multitude of various kinds of coacervates being formed in the primeval ocean. Many would be formed from comingled nucleic acids and proteins. All would attract various compounds from the water. Those that attracted a certain balance of compounds would grow. Those that failed to do this would either remain unchanged in size or would disappear. The growing drops eventually would break up into smaller drops by the action of waves and other forces. Thus, these drops would multiply in a crude way. During this time, the relationship between nucleic acids and the production of enzymes would be established, in whatever way it occurred. Those droplets with the most effective combination of compounds would grow and "reproduce," and thus a kind of rough natural selection, or "chemical selection," would cause a constant evolution toward cells as we know them today.

An alternative possibility for the development of the first protocells is suggested by the work of Fox and his associates. Fox, as the reader will recall, showed that amino acids can be synthesized using heat energy, and that a proteinlike material, proteinoid, can be formed from dry amino acids by heat. He theorizes that the earliest proteins might have been formed by heat from such sources as volcanic rocks or the warm rock surfaces around hot springs. (Figure 10–1.)

A particularly exciting development in Fox's work is the discovery that proteinoid has the power, under the right conditions, to form itself into microscopic-sized spheres, which Fox terms "microspheres." These globules share certain properties with cells and in the opinion of some scientists are more likely candidates for the role of protocells than Oparin's coacervates. (Figure 10–2.)

The microspheres are formed when proteinoid is dissolved in hot or warm water, which then is allowed to cool. Some of the material comes out of solution to form the tiny globules. Fox and his associates have carried out demonstrations to

10–1 Creating proteinoid by placing amino acids (top) on a heated rock. Bottom photo shows formed proteinoid.

10–2 Proteinoid microspheres as revealed by the electron microscope.

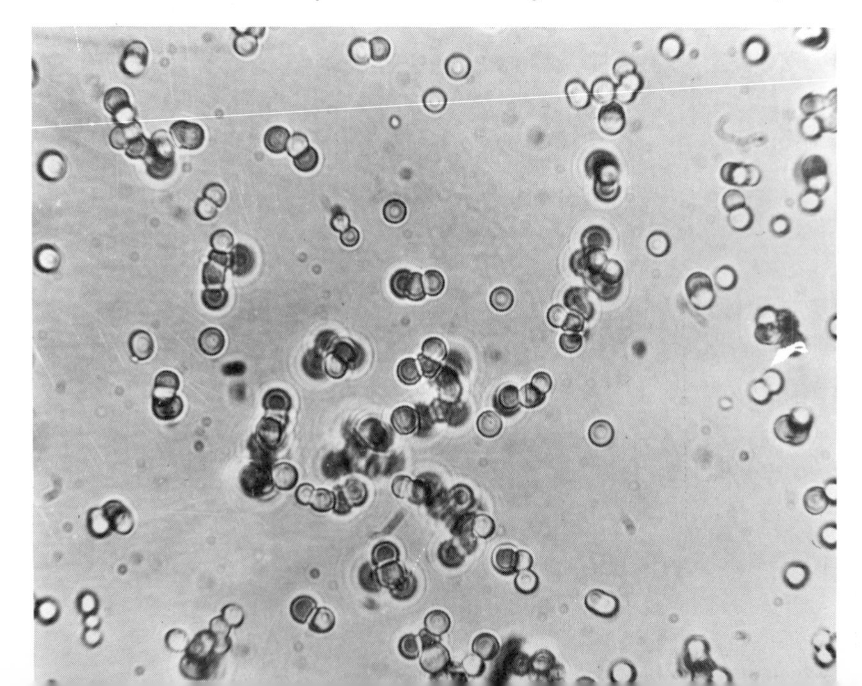

show how simply microspheres may be created. In one experiment, a mixture of dry amino acids was placed in a depression in a piece of preheated lava. The powder melted and gave off steam. This steam was water formed as a by-product of peptide linkages. The powder was converted into a sticky, amber-colored "syrup," proteinoid. Twenty minutes after the start of the demonstration, a shower of water was used to simulate rainfall on the rock. The water that ran off was cloudy and contained many microspheres. It is not hard to imagine proteinoids being formed on hot rocks on the early Earth and then being transformed into microspheres by rain that also washes the globules into a nearby body of water, such as a hot spring.

How do microspheres resemble cells? For one thing, while Oparin's coacervates are less stable than cells and tend to break up under stress, the microspheres are quite stable. They maintain their shape over the many weeks required to study them, and they can be centrifuged like bacteria without breaking up. They are actually about the same shape and size as coccoid bacteria, and can be dyed with Gram stain, a characteristic of some kinds of bacteria. What is perhaps most significant is that the microspheres display the ability to "reproduce" under certain conditions. If the microspheres are kept in the solution in which they were formed, after about a week they bud in a manner that reminds one of the budding of yeast cells when they reproduce. The buds on the sphere can be detached easily by electrical, thermal, or mechanical shock. If a fresh solution of proteinoid is prepared and the buds are placed in it, the proteinoid will come out of solution and be deposited on the buds. The buds grow in size until they are of normal bulk. After a certain time, they, too, form buds. A new cycle of "reproduction" has begun.

The researches being conducted by Fox have shown that amino acids can be formed abiogenetically by heat; that heat also can convert amino acids into proteinlike material; and that the material in turn can form particles with some of the properties of cells. The sequence demonstrates matter being boosted progressively into higher stages of organization. Did the sequence take place on the early Earth, and was it a prelude to life? No one knows, but certainly the laboratory facts are suggestive, and they are spurring a great deal of further research.

11

SPECULATIONS

FOLLOWING ARE SOME problem areas where scientists may have theories but few definite answers. Each area will require much more research.

Energy sources for the first organism: In modern cells, ATP serves as a storehouse for energy released by the breakdown of food molecules. We know from laboratory experiments that ATP probably was created abiogenetically in the early ocean. Carl Sagan has estimated that enough ATP was synthesized per square centimeter of ocean surface to provide energy for a population of some 20,000 bacteria. This ATP might have served to provide energy to early organisms without the necessity of their breaking down other molecules. Only when the abiogenetically formed ATP was exhausted would organisms have had to develop ways to create it within the cell.

The first food sources after ATP may have been other abiogenetically formed molecules, such as glucose, dissolved in the ocean "soup." Thus, the first organisms were heterotrophs, creatures that exist on organic matter already formed. With a growing ocean population, abiogenetically formed foodstuffs would eventually be used up. Then evolution of mechanisms to create food must have been necessary. Foremost among these was photosynthesis, the use of the energy of sunlight to produce sugar from water and carbon dioxide. Thus arose the autotrophs, those organisms that can produce their own food from inorganic substances. Some organisms remained heterotrophs, however, and lived by preying on the living or dead remains of other organisms. Scientists as yet do not know how photosynthesis was evolved.

Enzymes: Besides cellular form, one characteristic of life today is the use of protein enzymes to catalyze chemical reactions. In modern cells, the amino acid order of an enzyme is determined by the "code" of the nucleic acid molecules in the nucleus.

If the first proteins were formed abiogenetically, their amino acid sequences, one would think, would not follow any pattern but would be random. In that case, it would seem to be something of an accident if a protein had any catalytic power. However, the whole process may be less random than previously thought. Among individual amino acids, some tend more readily than others to form chains. These seem to be the ones most abundant in living systems. Thus, there may be a built-in bias in abiogenetic protein-making that encourages production of molecules with enzymatic activity. It could be significant that researchers have found that Fox's proteinoids show some catalytic powers.

A possible alternative or supplement to protein enzymes may have been inorganic catalysts. Many elements and compounds promote chemical reactions without themselves being used up. The metals, such as zinc, iron, copper, and magnesium, are often very active in this way. A number of modern enzymes include metal atoms as coenzymes. Such inorganic substances must have been present in considerable quantities in the primeval ocean "soup," and in mudbanks in shallow waters. They could have helped catalyze many chemical reactions while the more modern protein enzymes were being developed through evolution.

Life involves a series of related chemical reactions. These reactions must be at least roughly coordinated, and this implies a system of control in the organism. In modern cells, the control is provided by DNA molecules, which specify what enzymes can be produced and direct their manufacture.

The nucleic acids: We have already seen that primitive nucleic acids could have been built up abiogenetically from ingredients in the primeval soup. It is impossible at this time, however, for scientists to visualize just how these primitive molecules could have become linked into the life process. In the modern cell, DNA forms part of a closed cycle. For the DNA to direct cell operations and reproduce itself, certain enzymes must be present. The production of these enzymes, in turn, depends upon the presence of the DNA. Neither system appears to be able to get along without the other.

It is possible that the first organisms were able to get along without nucleic acids. They may have used some alternative system which we at present are not familiar with. Scientists studying the sheep disease called scrapie believe that it is caused by an unusual microbe that apparently lacks nucleic acids. Could this microbe be a holdover from more primitive organisms?

In most organisms today, the protein-formation process starts with the DNA in the nucleus, which directs the formation of messenger RNA, which in turn moves out into the cytoplasm to direct the synthesis of proteins. This elaborate process may be the result of billions of years of evolution, and the first system may have been much simpler. Many viruses contain no DNA. Their genetic material is single-stranded RNA. When this RNA enters a cell, it acts as its own messenger to direct the synthesis of proteins. Haldane suggests that the first organism may have consisted only of a short strand of RNA containing just enough information to direct the synthesis of one multipurpose enzyme. This enzyme could catalyze both the synthesis of more enzyme and the self-replication of the RNA. In Haldane's view, the first organism created artificially in the laboratory may follow these specifications.

Reproduction: A single cell can exist only so long before it meets with a fatal mishap of one kind or another. So, for life to maintain itself on our planet, it had to multiply through reproduction. The process of reproduction had to be accurate enough so that the important structures and control processes were handed down to the next generation. But absolutely accurate reproduction would have meant a dead-end street for life, because conditions on Earth have changed continuously from earliest times, and with no variations in heredity, life could not have adapted to a changing environment. As it is, there are definite variations among offspring, and these variations help to insure that there will be individual organisms ready to meet new conditions and survive in them.

In modern cells, the twin functions of heredity and variations are carried out by the DNA. By its ability to make copies of itself, the DNA molecule enables cell fission to take place and insures that each daughter cell will inherit needed characteristics. But, because the DNA is liable to certain kinds of damage, and because it sometimes makes errors in copying itself, there is room in the reproduction process for genetic variation.

Scientists at the present time find it difficult to visualize the evolutionary steps in the development of the reproductive process. It may be that the first organisms did not make use of nucleic acid in reproduction. The first form of multiplication may have been a crude mechanical process. For example, if Oparin's coacervates truly resemble the first protocells, the earliest type of reproduction might have been splitting through wave action or other outside forces. Another alternative is suggested by Fox's experiments with the budding proteinoid microspheres.

The role of chance: One topic often discussed by scientists in this field of research is the role of chance in the origin of life. Before the days of modern biochemistry, scientists often assumed that somehow life arose from a chance meeting of the right atoms and molecules. However, modern research shows that the cell and its chemistry are so complex that, statistically speaking, the chances of a cell's being formed by the fortuitous collision of atoms are practically nil.

Take, for example, the primitive RNA molecule that Haldane suggests may have been used by the first organism. Haldane has calculated that, assuming that nucleosides are assembled in random order, the chance of the right sequence's emerging would be somewhere around 1 in 1,000,000,000,000,000,000,000,000,000,000,000,000,000. Haldane feels that this means that something other than chance must have operated to produce that primitive molecule.

Many scientists, including Haldane, suspect that as-yet-unknown factors "loaded the dice" on the side of life. They feel that just as the amino acid sequence in a protein determines the three-dimensional shape and catalytic activity of the molecule, so the higher structures of life may arise more or less automatically from simpler ingredients. Dr. Barghoorn believes that the rise of life must have been a highly probable and geologically rapid event. Chemist Richard Lemmon of the University of California states that life possibly could have arisen in the space of a year, given the right conditions.

12

LIFE'S EFFECTS ON OUR PLANET

FEW PEOPLE REALIZE how profoundly living organisms have modified our planet. The modifications go far beyond the green mantle covering the hills and valleys, far beyond the great cities built by man. Many rock formations are due to plant and animal life. The coal beds found in many regions are formed from the carbon of ferns and other plants. It is thought that microbes may have caused the deposit of the great formations of iron ores. The extensive limestone beds of the world are mostly formed from the shells of small ocean animals. While some organisms help build up rocks, others help destroy them. Lichens aid in the weathering of rocks by chemically attacking them, and trees and other higher plants help break rocks apart by sending growing roots deep into cracks. Earthworms constantly till the soil.

Perhaps the single greatest effect of life has been upon the planet's atmosphere. Once scientists accepted the idea that the primeval atmosphere contained little or no free oxygen, the question naturally arose as to how the present oxygen-rich atmosphere developed. It is known that some free oxygen is being released continuously in the upper atmosphere by the action of ultraviolet light on water vapor. However, the rate at which atmospheric oxygen is used up in oxidation of minerals of the Earth's crust appears to be much greater than the rate at which UV light produces it. Some other source of oxygen is needed.

In recent years, many scientists have come to the conclusion that most of the oxygen in the present atmosphere has been produced by photosynthesis. In the early 1960's, a comprehensive theory of how our present atmosphere evolved was presented by the American scientists L. C. Marshall and Lloyd Berkner.

The two men calculated that in the early stages of Earth's history, the ultraviolet light radiation would be so intense that killing amounts of it would penetrate to a depth of 5 to 10 yards in bodies of water. Primitive free-floating organisms would have no mechanism to maintain a constant depth. Such free-floating cells in the open ocean would be at the mercy of convection currents that would either sweep them up into the fatal ultraviolet zone or else downward into the equally fatal dark cold depths beyond the reach of visible light. This consideration, the two scientists argued, suggests that the early primitive plants and animals were bottom-living creatures existing in shallow waters. Less than 1 per cent of the total ocean area would be livable. An example of the bottom-living organisms of that period may be the algae that formed the Pre-Cambrian stromatolites. Another scientist, Alfred Fischer of Princeton University, has suggested that the limestone or silica layers that make up the stromatolites may represent the algae's defense against ultraviolet rays. Fischer also suggests that the first oxygen-using animals may have arisen at this time in association with isolated algae colonies (Figure 12–1). These may have included certain bacteria, sponges, and other simple, soft-bodied animals. These primitive animals were linked to the plant colonies by their need for the oxygen produced by the algae and dissolved in the surrounding water.

The plants in the early shallow coastal waters gradually produced enough oxygen to bring the atmospheric oxygen level to about 1 per cent of its present value. Although such an oxygen level may seem very low, it had revolutionary consequences for life on our planet. For it provided enough of an "umbrella" for ultraviolet rays so that the rays were too weak to penetrate more than the top inch or so of the ocean. This meant that

12–1 *The steps in the build-up of oxygen on Earth. The dots represent oxygen molecules. The round circles represent various oxygen-using animals.*

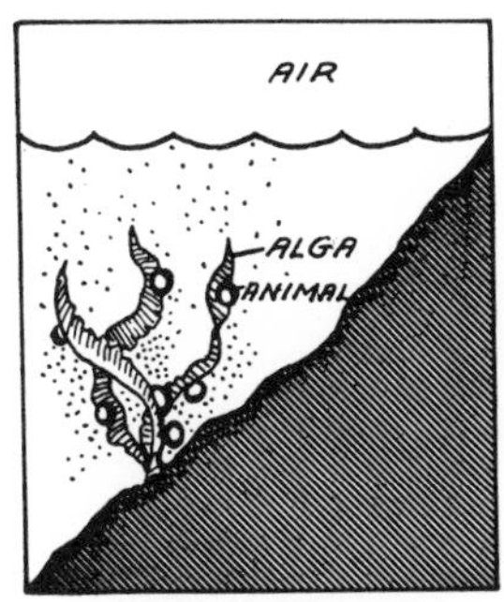

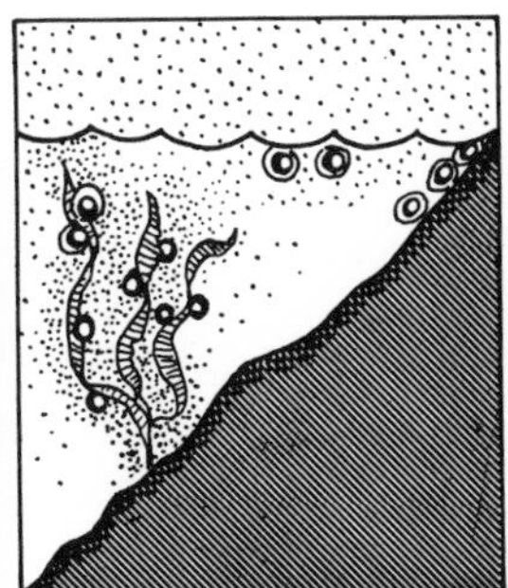

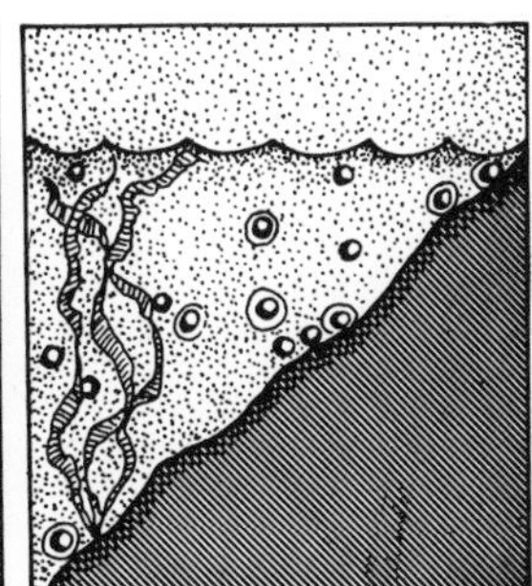

free-living organisms could spread with some safety throughout the ocean.

The next major step in the evolution of our atmosphere occurred around the Silurian period. This time saw the appearance of primitive land animals and plants in the fossil record. Berkner and Marshall argued that this evolutionary step reflected the fact that the oxygen concentration in the atmosphere had reached a level about 10 per cent that of the present value. This reduced ultraviolet radiation to the point where plants and animals could emerge from the water into the open air. Many of the early land animals had external coats of some sort, and this may have been an evolutionary adaptation to the remaining ultraviolet radiation. Fischer has proposed that the widespread move to the land was preceded by early colonization of certain protected land environments. "Shade oases" may have been the sites where the first land plants developed. When the UV level dropped far enough, the plants could spread outward from these isolated locations and intermingle. The development of land plants further increased the oxygen level.

13

LIFE IN THE UNIVERSE

IN MEDIEVAL TIMES, Earth was considered the center of the universe and the seat of created life. Our globe was a kind of throne for mankind, and the sun, moon, planets, and stars were moving lights set in the heavens to provide illumination, mark the passage of time, and provide visible evidence of the glory of the Creator.

The work of Copernicus, Galileo, and others overturned this comfortable and snug scheme. The sun was made the center of the solar system, and the planets circled it in democratic equality, none more important than the others. The stars were shown to be inconceivably distant suns that might even have their own planetary families. With these developments, philosophers began to speculate that perhaps Earth was not the only home of life in creation. Perhaps God had created other creatures on other worlds.

The new outlook is expressed by the English philosopher Henry Moore in his poem *The Argument of Democritus Platonissans,* or *The Infinitie of Worlds,* published in 1646:

> "My nimble mind this clammie clod doth leave,
> And lightly stepping on from starre to starre
> Swifter than lightning, passeth wide and farre,
> Measuring th' unbounded Heavens and wastfull
> (unfrequented) skie . . ."

Moore argues in his poem that "infinity of worlds there be" and that the stars are suns with planets of their own. Under the influence of sunlight and moisture, these planets very likely have produced life: "grasse, flowers, hearbs, trees" and "flies, birds, men, and beasts."

On Earth, life depends upon the presence of water, an atmosphere, and moderate temperatures. If all life demands a similar environment, most planets and satellites in the solar system must be lifeless. The moon, for example, has virtually no free water and no atmosphere, and its temperature fluctuates between wide extremes of searing heat during the day and freezing cold during the night. Thus, even before direct examination of the moon by space craft and men, scientists were fairly sure that Earth-type life could not exist on our planet's natural satellite.

The same objections apply to Mercury, the planet nearest the sun. Mercury is believed to have no atmosphere or water.

For many decades, researchers had high hopes that life might exist on Venus, whose orbit lies between that of Mercury and Earth. Venus appears in our night sky either as the Morning Star or the Evening Star, depending on the time of the year. In some ways, it is our sister planet, close to Earth in size and mass. In addition, it has an atmosphere, and its distance from the sun is such that many astronomers thought that the planet's temperature might be hospitable to life.

Venus has been called the "mystery planet" because an almost featureless layer of clouds in its atmosphere shields the surface from telescopic view. While there may be small gaps in the cloud cover, these are too small to be of value in observing the planet from Earth. For a long time, the cloud layer prevented astronomers from measuring the diameter of the solid globe of Venus; they could measure only the diameter of the disk visible in their telescopes, which of course included the clouds. Also, by preventing astronomers from viewing the movement of surface features, the cloud layer kept them from accurately measuring the rotation of the planet on its axis. However, the new science of radar astronomy has helped remove some of the mystery. Bursts of radio waves are beamed at the planet. These penetrate through the cloud cover and reach the solid surface. A part of the energy of each burst is reflected from the surface much as light is reflected from a mirror. These radio reflections, or echoes, can be picked up by sensitive radio telescopes back on Earth. By study of the radio echoes, astronomers can estimate the diameter of the solid part of Venus. This turns out to be about 7502 miles, compared with Earth's 7926-mile diameter.

Radio studies also give information about the rotation of Venus. It appears that the planet has a unique rotation. An observer looking down from above the plane of the solar system would see all the planets but Venus spinning in a counterclockwise direction. Venus is rotating slowly in the reverse direction. Scientists as yet do not know why this should happen; perhaps the gravitational influence of Earth is responsible. The Venusian days and nights are months long, for the planet takes 257 Earth days to make a single rotation.

Venus's rotation is not the only way in which it differs radically from Earth. Like other material objects in our universe, Venus emits some heat and radio energy of its own. Earth-based radio telescopes can pick up this radiation, and from it scientists can estimate the planet's temperature. Such estimates made in the early 1960's showed that the planet might have a very hot surface temperature, perhaps as hot as molten lead. This was a significant discovery, for water cannot exist as a liquid at such temperatures, and this made it doubtful that water-based life could survive on the Venusian surface. Some scientists doubted the reliability of the estimates, however, until a series of space probes by the United States and the Soviet Union confirmed them.

The first successful probe to collect information about Venus was made by Mariner II, launched by the United States in 1962. Mariner II was sent on a course that took it near the planet. As it passed by, instruments aboard the craft gathered data. Among these data were measurements of heat emissions from the planet, and these measurements confirmed the fact that the surface of Venus was very hot. In June 1967, the United States and the Soviet Union each launched a Venus probe. Both arrived in the neighborhood of Venus five months later. The American craft, Mariner V, like its predecessor, swept by the planet at close range, gathering data. The Soviet craft, Venera IV, however, ejected a capsule that plunged into the planet's atmosphere and parachuted to a "soft landing" on the surface. The capsule collected a great deal of information as it descended through the cloud layer and approached the surface.

Before the two flights, many astronomers believed that Venus's atmosphere, like Earth's, probably was largely nitrogen. Evidence gathered by spectroscopic study of sunlight reflected from Venus indicated that the atmosphere contained carbon dioxide also. The two probes revealed, to the surprise of some researchers, that carbon dioxide is the major ingredient of the Venusian atmosphere, making up perhaps 90 per cent. The remainder is probably mostly nitrogen or argon, with traces of other gases. Venera IV measurements showed that oxygen may make up about 1 per cent of the atmosphere. There also are traces of water vapor, but Venus appears to be drier than the Sahara Desert. In the upper atmosphere, temperatures are much lower than they are near the surface. Some researchers have proposed that the clouds of Venus might be made up of water droplets or ice crystals.

One of the most interesting results of the two space probes is the discovery that the Venusian atmosphere is much, much denser than Earth's atmosphere. The air pressure at the surface is 75 to 100 times as great as normal atmospheric pressure on our planet. Human explorers will have to wear special equipment to protect them from the pressure, much as divers do, since it will be equivalent to the water pressure more than one half mile deep in the ocean.

The dense atmosphere causes light to play strange tricks

on Venus. A light beam is sharply bent as it passes through the thick air. Even on the night side of Venus, the sky glows with light that has been refracted around the globe from the day side. An observer standing on a flat plain on Venus would have the illusion that he was in a great bowl, with the horizon above eye level.

The high temperatures and apparent desertlike conditions of Venus make the outlook for finding life on that planet rather discouraging. Certainly Earth-type life could not survive for more than a moment unprotected on the Venusian surface near the equator. Some scientists have suggested that conditions may be more favorable to life in the cooler polar regions or in the upper atmosphere. Dr. Carl Sagon has proposed that, if the clouds of Venus are made up of water, life could have originated in the atmosphere and could have evolved means of maintaining itself aloft. He suggests that Venusian organisms could have balloonlike "float bladders" filled with the light gas hydrogen. These bladders would keep the creatures supported in the atmosphere in the region where liquid water droplets could provide moisture to them. In the presence of sunlight, water, and carbon dioxide, food could be created by photosynthesis. Needed minerals could be obtained from dust blown up from the Venusian surface. Scientists have no evidence at the present time, however, that such organisms actually do exist.

Earth is the third planet from the sun, and Mars (Figure 13–1) is fourth. The Red Planet, so called because of the reddish tone of its surface, has long been considered the most likely abode for life in our solar system, besides Earth. Mars

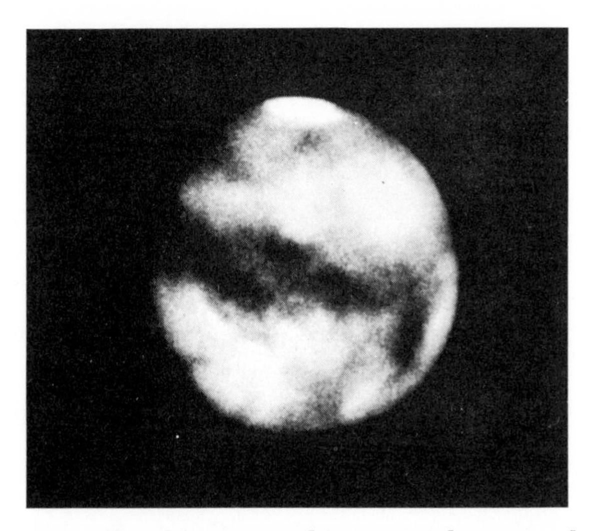

13–1 The planet Mars, showing a polar cap and some of the dark "blue-green" areas.

is considerably smaller than Earth, with a diameter somewhat over half that of Earth and a total mass only about one-tenth as great. Due to its smaller mass, Mars has a lesser gravitational pull than Earth and cannot keep as thick a blanket of air around it. In 1965 the United States space craft Mariner IV flew near the planet to gather data. As a result of the flight the scientists found that the air pressure at the Martian surface is surprisingly low, less than one-hundredth that of the Earth. The main atmospheric ingredient turned out to be carbon dioxide, which makes up 50 to 80 per cent of the air. Most of the rest is probably argon or nitrogen, or a mixture of these two gases. There probably is a trace of oxygen but not enough to support human life.

Observations from Earth show that Mars often has varying numbers of white clouds in its atmosphere. These may appear as large cloud systems in the equatorial or temperate zones of Mars, or as a thick white shroud over the polar region in the hemisphere where winter is taking place. Mists appear from time to time in various regions of the planet. A white polar cap also forms in each hemisphere of Mars during that hemisphere's winter. When the cold season comes to the hemisphere, thick clouds cover the polar region and linger there for months. In the spring, the clouds clear and reveal a polar cap, which then grows smaller and eventually disappears as the hemisphere warms.

The clouds and icecaps have convinced many scientists that water must exist on Mars. Spectrographic study of reflected light from the planet seems to show indications of water vapor, but only a small amount. The atmosphere appears to be much drier than desert air here on Earth. For a number of reasons, scientists doubt that liquid water exists on the surface of Mars. The clouds and icecaps are believed to be made up of ice crystals. When the temperature rises enough to melt these crystals, they evaporate rapidly into the thin Martian air without remaining long in the liquid state.

Because Mars is 1.5 times as far from the Sun as Earth, it receives less heat than our planet. In addition, the thinness of the air and lack of water and clouds enable heat to escape rapidly from the Martian surface. Even at high noon at the equator, the surface temperature probably does not rise much above 80 degrees Fahrenheit, and the air temperature is probably considerably cooler than that. At night, the surface temperature likely drops to 90 degrees F. below zero. We might compare this with the average temperature of −73 degrees F. during the long winter night at the South Pole of Earth.

Various surface features are visible on Mars. There are large reddish areas believed to be deserts. From time to time, moving yellow clouds appear in the Martian atmosphere. These are probably dust storms stirred up by winds in the desert regions. The ruddy color of the deserts is due to the presence of rusty iron compounds in the soil.

Much of the speculation about life on Mars has centered around large dark regions that are spotted across the surface of the planet. Most observers say that they are blue-green in color. The areas in each hemisphere appear to deepen in shade during the Martian spring, as the icecap retreats. This has led many scientists to suggest that the dark regions are areas of vegetation that have seasonal changes in foliage.

The question arises as to what kind of vegetation could best withstand the rigorous climate of Mars, with its thin, cold, dry air and desert surface conditions. Various scientists have experimented with microorganisms placed under simulated Martian conditions. These experiments show that the microorganisms not only can survive but can reproduce in such an environment. Somewhat higher forms of life, such as lichens, also show amazing tenacity of life under adverse conditions. Lichens are found both in the Sahara and in Antarctica. However, some scientists doubt that such primitive plants as bacteria and lichens could cause the dark regions of Mars and the seasonal changes in hue. Lichens, for example, show little color change from season to season. It is possible that higher forms of plants, with leafy foliages, have evolved on Mars despite the unfavorable conditions. Such plants might have developed special mechanisms for conserving water and protecting themselves from extreme cold.

Much has been written about the "canals" of Mars. These are streaks seeming to link some of the blue-green regions of Mars. For many years, there was considerable talk about the canals being channels built by intelligent beings. However, this seems doubtful. Conditions on Mars seem totally unsuitable for the development of higher forms of animal life. Scientists do not know what the canals are; they may be natural valleys or faults, or may even be largely optical illusions.

The Mariner IV carried cameras which took 22 still pictures of the Martian surface (Figure 13–2) from a distance varying between 10,500 and 6118 miles. These pictures were transmitted back to Earth by radio. The most interesting fact revealed by the pictures was that Mars is covered with a hodgepodge of meteorite craters that in the photographs ranged from 3 to 75 miles in diameter. This was new evidence of the dryness of the Martian surface, for on Earth meteorite craters are smoothed down and eventually eliminated by natural weathering processes. On Mars, however, the craters have lasted for millions of years. The pictures did not show any obvious canal-like markings, but one photograph did show a marking that could be interpreted as a depressed strip of land. The photographs were taken from such a distance that scientists did not expect them to reveal any evidence of vegetation, and they did not.

Our space scientists hope that sometime in the 1970's they

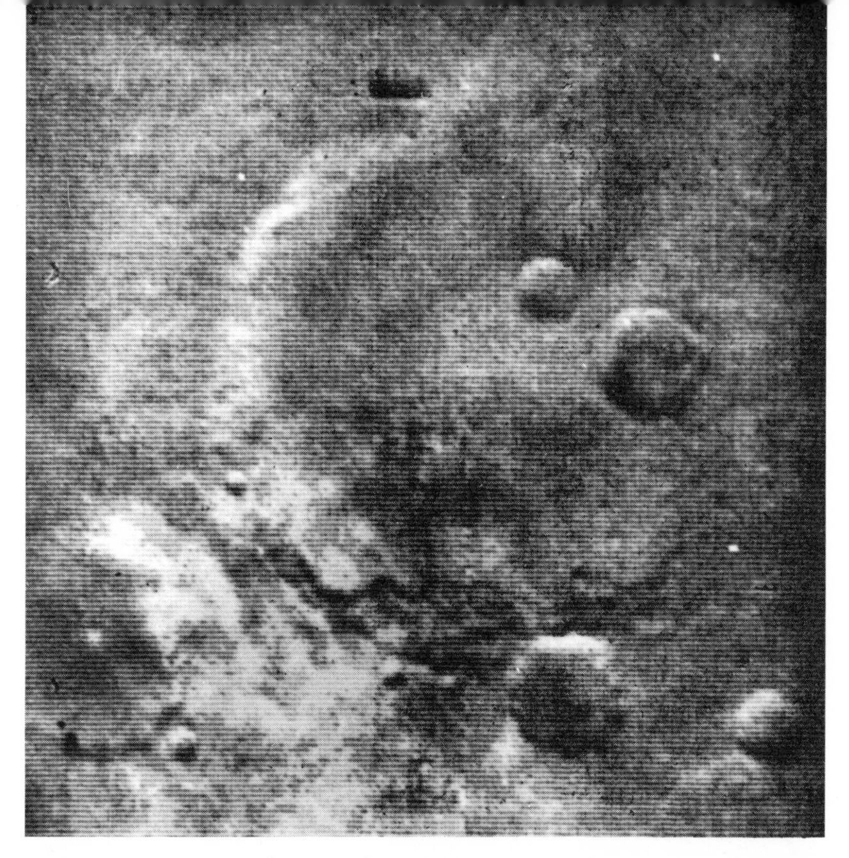

13–2 A Mariner IV close-up photograph of Mars, showing several craters. Taken from a distance of about 7800 miles.

can send a series of space craft to Mars to investigate the possibility of life. In the Voyager program, as it is called, craft would make soft landings on the planet to carry out various chemical and biological tests for life. Until that time, the question of life on Mars is likely to remain mostly in the realm of speculation.

What about the planets beyond Mars? The next four planets, often called the giant planets, are much larger than Earth. In order of their distances from the sun they are: Jupiter, with a mass 315 times that of Earth; Saturn, the ringed planet, equal to 94 Earth masses; Uranus, about 14 Earth masses; and Neptune, about 17 Earth masses. Beyond the giant planets lies the ninth member of our solar system, Pluto, so distant from the sun that its mass cannot be accurately calculated. Pluto receives so little of the sun's heat that it probably is a solid lump of rock and frozen gases, a very unlikely site for life. The giant planets, however, have certain possibilities for life, particularly Jupiter (Figure 13–3).

Jupiter is believed to be made up of the same elements of which the primeval solar cloud was composed before it condensed into the sun and planets. This means that the planet is mainly hydrogen and hydrogen compounds. The planet's atmosphere is thought to be about 2500 miles deep;

13–3 *The planet Jupiter.*

it is largely ammonia and hydrogen (Figure 13–4). The core of Jupiter is hydrogen compressed into the solid state by the crushing burden of the overlying atmosphere.

Jupiter is comparatively distant from the sun and its outer layers are very cold, with the topmost part of the atmosphere thought to be made up of frozen ammonia crystals. Due to increasing pressure, the temperature rises farther down in the atmosphere, however, and 1800 miles down there is a region where Earthlike temperatures may exist. Here, liquid and gaseous water exists along with ammonia and methane. These chemicals, some scientists think, could provide the basic ingredients for life on Jupiter.

A source of energy is needed to build up the molecules of life. Such energy is thought to exist in Jupiter's atmosphere in the form of great electrical discharges, lightning.

In a paper presented before the American Chemical Society

13–4 *Jupiter's atmosphere. Not to scale.*

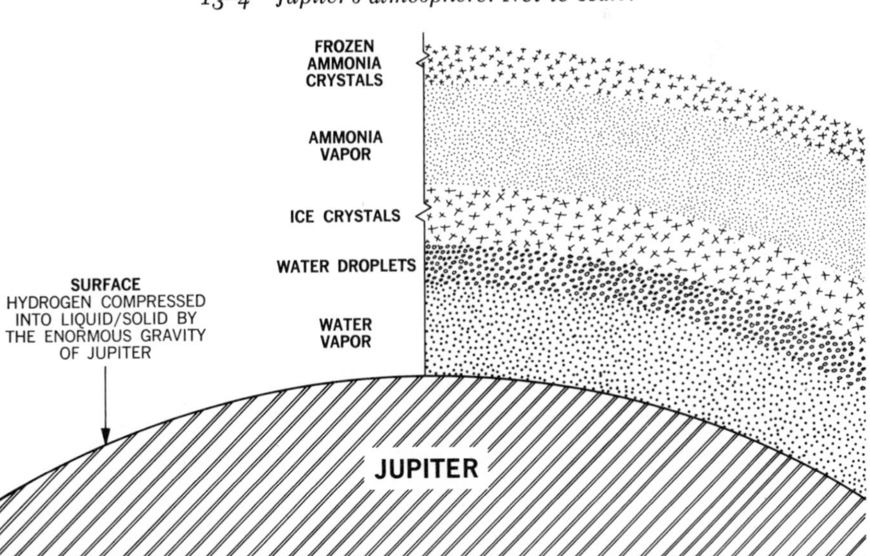

in 1967, Dr. Cyril Ponnamperuma and Fritz Woeller, both of the National Aeronautics and Space Administration, described experiments with a simulated Jupiter atmosphere. The researchers used electrical discharges to spark chemical reactions in a mixture of ammonia and methane held at the low temperature of the outer atmosphere of Jupiter, about 356 degrees below zero. They found that a number of organic building blocks were created, which needed only the addition of water to form even more complex molecules. The researchers also simulated the warmer lower layer of the atmosphere where liquid water is thought to exist. The electrical discharges produced organic molecules here, too. Raising the pressure demonstrated that such molecules could be formed even at the crushing pressures found deep in the atmosphere of the giant planet.

Until unmanned space craft and astronauts explore the planets, we will not be definitely sure of what organic materials may be found on them. We already have another class of space objects close at hand, however, the meteorites. These are stony or metallic objects that fall to Earth's surface from space. Space contains a considerable amount of dust and rocks left over from the origin of the solar system. Bits of material are constantly entering Earth's atmosphere. Quite often, they are moving at high speed relative to Earth, and air friction heats them to incandescence. We see these white-hot objects streaking through the night sky and call them shooting stars, or meteors. Most meteors are so small that they vaporize before reaching the ground. A few, however, are large enough so that they lose only part of their mass as they fall. These reach the ground and are called meteorites when they are found and identified.

About three out of every hundred meteorites contain considerable carbon. The first known stone of this class fell in 1806 in Alais, France. It was sent to the great Swedish chemist Berzelius, who in 1834 examined it chemically. He found a remarkable resemblance between the carbonaceous material of the meteorite and earthly biological material. He asked, "Does this carbonaceous . . . material truly contain humus or a trace of other organic compounds? Does this possibly give a hint concerning the presence of organic structures in other planetary bodies?"

On a May evening in 1864, the residents of Orgueil, France, saw a bright meteor in the sky and heard explosive sounds. About 20 fragments of the space visitor were picked up soon afterward over a 2-mile-square area.

The Orgueil stones have been one of the most intensively studied group of meteorite fragments. The French scientist S. Cloez analyzed a fragment soon after the fall and found organic matter resembling peat, lignite, and soil organic matter. In addition to his studies, more than 40 other examinations were made of the fragments between 1864 and 1894. Samples of the meteorite were distributed to several museums for preservation, and these samples continue to provide investigators with material for study. There has been a great deal of recent interest in the Orgueil meteorite.

In 1961, three American chemists reported results of a new analysis of a fragment of the Orgueil meteorite obtained from the Museum of Natural History in New York City. They used the mass spectroscope, a sophisticated instrument of modern chemistry that allows researchers to detect very small traces of compounds, sort them out, and measure their concentrations. The three chemists said that they had identified hydrocarbon compounds in the meteorite fragment similar to those found in fossilized organic remains. Other workers have since reported finding such substances as amino acids and fatty acids.

In addition, some researchers have found microscopic structures in the Orgueil and other meteorites that they feel resemble fossilized algae or bacteria. The nature of these microstructures is a matter of much dispute, some believing that they are truly fossilized microbes, others being of the opinion that they were formed by natural physical processes during the birth of the meteorites or during their heated descent to the Earth.

Just about all scientists agree that the carbonaceous meteorites contain organic materials of various kinds. How can these materials be explained? Several hypotheses have been offered:

1. *The organic substances are the result of contamination by earthly biological agents such as microbes.* While this hypothesis may explain some of the compounds found in the carbon-rich meteorites, it does not seem adequate to explain all the organic-type materials found in the stones.

2. *A variation of this explanation is offered by Harold Urey.* He thinks that the carbonaceous meteorites may have come from the moon, perhaps ejected into space by volcanic action or by the impact of meteors. Among the various

theories of the moon's formation there is one that holds that the moon once was part of Earth and broke away from it. Another theory is that the moon originally was not a satellite but was captured by Earth's gravity. Urey thinks that during the moon's escape from or capture by the Earth, the lunar surface may have been contaminated by ocean water containing living organisms. If this actually occurred, then materials ejected from the lunar surface would carry traces of organic material. Tests of lunar rocks brought back to Earth by astronauts may either support or tend to disprove this hypothesis.

3. *Organic compounds in the carbonaceous meteorites originated from living things on some astronomical body other than Earth.* The meteorites, according to this hypothesis, could be fragments of a planet or asteroid that once supported life.

4. *The compounds were formed abiogenetically.* If the meteorites condensed from the gases and dust of the primeval solar system, there is a good chance that inorganic chemical processes could have produced at least some of the compounds found in the meteorites, just as scientists using sparking chambers have been able to form such compounds. This explanation might still apply if the meteorites are fragments of a larger body. In connection with this, we might mention studies that scientists have made of comets, those "hairy stars" consisting of rocks, dust, and frozen gases that partly evaporate to form a spectacular tail when the comet nears the sun. Comets are members of the solar system, although their looping orbits carry them so far from the sun that they can dis-

appear for years. Spectroscopic analysis of reflected light from comets shows that they are composed of a number of elements, among them carbon, hydrogen, nitrogen, and oxygen, the basic elements of life. Astronomers further have found evidence that hydrocarbons exist in comets, and these must have been formed by abiogenetic processes.

What are the chances of life's existing outside of our solar system? Any planets circling other stars are too small and dark to be observed directly through our telescopes on Earth. However, there is indirect evidence that at least a few stars have one or more planets. Most stars are not motionless but are traveling in various directions in straight-line paths. A few stars show a curious kind of rhythmic wiggling in their forward motion, a little bit like the side-to-side motion of a tight-rope walker. Astronomers believe that these perturbations in the motion of a star are due to the presence of a "dark companion" orbiting it, a companion too small to shine by its own light but large enough to influence gravitationally the star it circles. To affect the star's motion strongly enough to be observed from Earth, such a companion must be considerably larger than the largest planet in our solar system, Jupiter. However, if such giant companions exist, why not smaller planets?

Present-day theories of star formation hold that many stars probably have planetary systems. Some of these systems must have Earth-type planets. It has been estimated that from 1 to 5 per cent of the stars in our galaxy may have planets able to support life. As George Wald puts it: "That would mean at least one billion such planets in our galaxy alone; and since there are about 100 million galaxies now within range of the most powerful telescopes, the number of planets suitable for life in the already observed universe may be of the order 10^{17} [Author's note: 1 followed by 17 zeroes]. This number is so vast—even if it were reduced a million times—as to make it difficult to avoid the conclusion that life is widespread in the universe."

Some scientists and science fiction writers have suggested that there may be life forms based upon other chemical systems than our own—where silicon might substitute for carbon, for example, or ammonia for water. There are fairly strong scientific arguments against each suggested alternate life system, but we do not know enough at present to dismiss these speculations entirely.

In any case, man almost certainly has neighbors in the universe and if he manages to avoid nuclear annihilation may someday encounter them. It is hard to imagine a greater challenge, a greater adventure.

APPENDIX A

ATOMS AND THEIR CHEMICAL BEHAVIOR

CHEMISTS HAVE DISCOVERED some 100-odd elements that combine together in various ways to form the substances around us and in us. An element is a substance that cannot be broken down chemically into simpler substances. Scientists have found that each element is made up of tiny particles called atoms, and that the differences between the elements are due to differences in the structure of their atoms.

Scientists originally thought of atoms as hard, impenetrable balls that could not be broken down into smaller particles. However, in our century it has been shown that an atom may consist of still tinier bits of matter known as subatomic particles. The first such particle to be discovered was the electron, a negatively charged bit of matter much lighter than the atom as a whole. It was found that most of the mass of an atom is concentrated in a central core, called the nucleus, which is surrounded by a cloud of one or more electrons. The lightest, simplest atom is that of hydrogen. This atom ordinarily consists of a nucleus about which a single electron orbits. The electron carries a negative electrical charge. The nucleus is positively charged. The positive charge just balances the negative charge, so that the atom as a whole is electrically neutral.

Scientists later found that the nucleus of the hydrogen atom is a single particle, which they called a proton. The next heaviest atom, that of helium, has more than a single particle in the nucleus. It has two protons and two other particles known as neutrons. As their name implies, neutrons are electrically neutral. Because of the presence of the two protons, the nucleus carries a double positive electrical charge. To balance this, two electrons circle the nucleus to render the atom as a whole neutral.

By progressively adding protons and neutrons to the nucleus, nature creates heavier and heavier atoms of other elements. With each new proton, an electron is added to balance the extra positive charge. When we reach a very heavy atom like that of uranium, we find 92 protons in the nucleus and about 146 neutrons. Circling the nucleus are 92 electrons.

Figure A–1 shows four representative atoms: hydrogen, helium, oxygen, and carbon. The electron orbits are shown as circles on the flat plane of the paper. In actuality, the electron paths trace out a three-dimensional sphere enclosing the

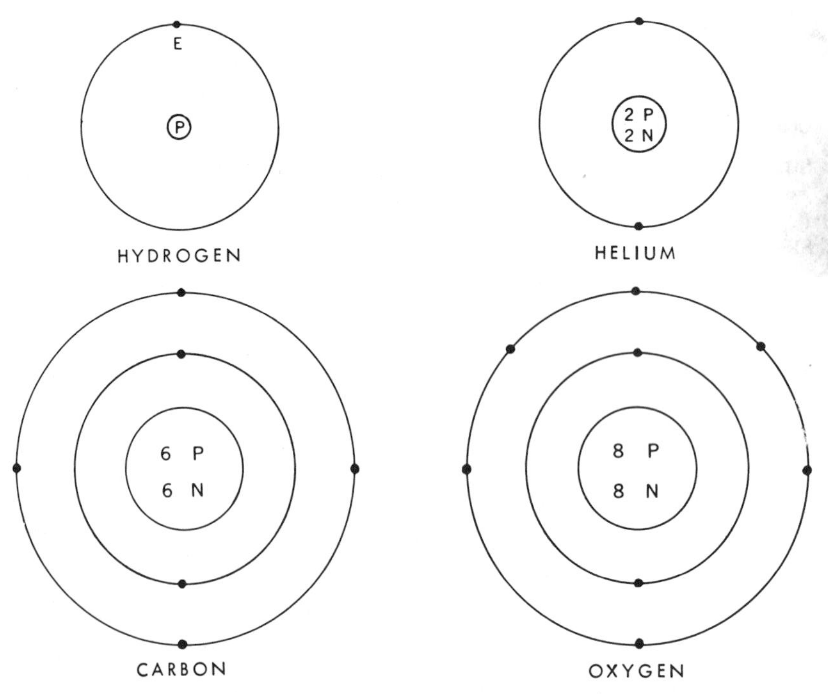

A–1 The structure of four common atoms.

nucleus. The electrons also do not follow exact orbits but wander a bit, at times being closer and at other times farther from the nucleus. However, an electron ordinarily stays within a certain range from the nucleus, and we speak of that range as the orbit.

Notice from the diagram that the electrons are arranged in successive layers, called shells, about the nucleus. The electrons in the outermost shell are in the suburbs, so to speak, of the atom. It is these electrons that are largely responsible for the chemical behavior of the atom. To understand something of this, let us examine the difference in chemical behavior between the hydrogen atom and the next heavier atom, that of helium. Both have only one electron shell, which serves as their outer shell. Helium has two electrons in the shell. Helium is chemically a very lazy element. It does not [illegible] together with other atoms, either of helium or other elements. It turns out that this chemical inertness is due to the fact that helium has two electrons in its outer shell. The presence of two electrons in the shell makes the helium atom "self-sufficient," with no tendency to combine with other atoms.

The case of hydrogen is different, however. Hydrogen has only one electron in its outer shell. It is not as stable as it would be if the shell contained two electrons. This gives the atom a kind of "hunger," if we may use the term, for an additional electron. Now, suppose that the hydrogen atom bumps into another hydrogen atom. Atom A will have a tendency to seize the electron of atom B in order to have a complete outer shell. Atom B, on the other hand, tries to seize the electron of atom A. Neither succeeds in stealing the other's electron. Rather, they cling together and share electrons. Each atom, in effect, has a stable outer shell because it has the use of two electrons. The two atoms actually merge their electron shells to form a single particle, the hydrogen molecule (Figure A–2).

The covalent bond, as it is called, is quite strong, and considerable energy must be used to separate the two atoms. Many of the molecules in the cell are formed largely by covalent bonds. In atoms heavier than helium, the "magic number" needed for a stable outer shell is not two but eight electrons. The oxygen atom, for example, has six outer elec-

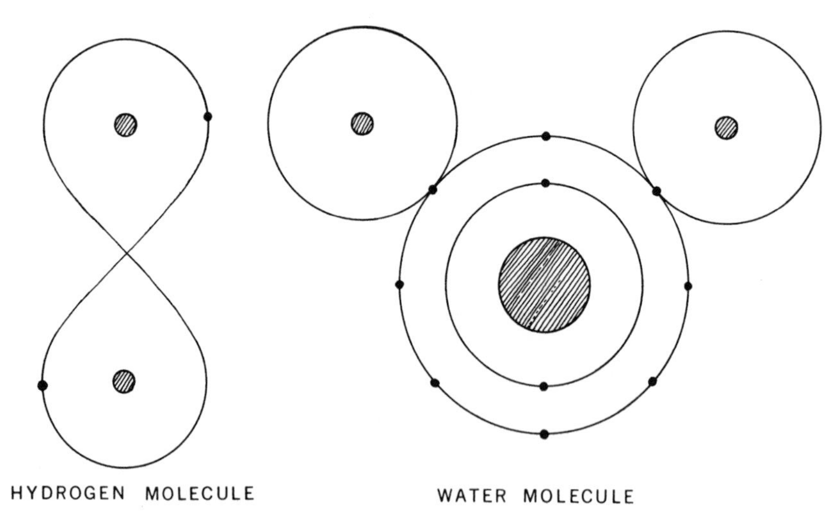

A–2 The hydrogen molecule and the water molecule.

trons and needs two more to achieve stability. This it can obtain by partly merging with two hydrogen atoms, each of which donates an electron to the oxygen, while the oxygen in turn donates an extra electron to each hydrogen atom. Thus, a molecule of water, H_2O, is formed (See Figure A–2).

Perhaps the single most important element in protoplasm is the carbon atom; its importance stems from the fact that it is especially versatile in forming covalent bonds, either with other carbon atoms or with atoms of other elements. Carbon has the ability to form an extraordinary number of different molecules, including the large, elaborate molecules that are characteristic of living things.

The carbon atom has four electrons in its outer shell, and it needs eight to form a stable shell. We can represent the carbon atom by the letter C, and the electrons of the outer shell by four dots placed around the letter:

```
  ·
· C ·
  ·
```

To gain a stable outer shell, the carbon atom needs to share four additional electrons. In the methane molecule, these electrons are donated by hydrogen atoms:

```
    H
    ··
H : C : H
    ··
    H
```

Each outer electron in the carbon is paired with an electron from a hydrogen atom. This pair of electrons is shared by the carbon and hydrogen. The carbon and hydrogen atoms both achieve stable shells.

In writing structural formulas, it is customary to indicate each pair of shared electrons—that is, each covalent bond—with a single dash. The methane molecule is shown in this way:

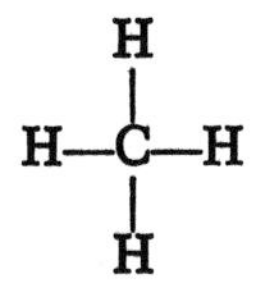

The carbon atom thus can form a total of four bonds.

The carbon atom can share more than a single pair of electrons with another atom. It can form a compound like ethylene, in which each carbon atom shares two electron pairs with the other, to form what is called a double bond:

$$\begin{matrix} H:C::C:H \\ \;\;\ddot{}\;\;\;\ddot{} \\ \;\;H\;\;H \end{matrix} \qquad \text{or} \qquad \begin{matrix} H—C{=}C—H \\ \;\;|\;\;\;\;| \\ \;\;H\;\;\;H \end{matrix}$$

Or, it can share three pairs of electrons to form what is called a triple bond, as in acetylene:

$$H:C:::C:H \qquad \text{or} \qquad H—C{\equiv}C—H$$

The covalent bond is not the only type of linkage between atoms. Another important type is the ionic bond, in which electrons are transferred from atom to atom instead of being shared. We should state at this point that outer electrons are often rather easily removed or added to atoms. A typical example occurs when an atom of sodium is brought into contact with an atom of chlorine (Figure A–3). The sodium atom has only one electron in its outer shell, while the chlorine has seven and lacks only one to complete a stable shell. In this case, the solitary electron in the outer shell of the sodium atom actually hops over to the other atom. This exposes the

A–3 How sodium and chlorine form ions and are attracted to each other because of their opposite charges.

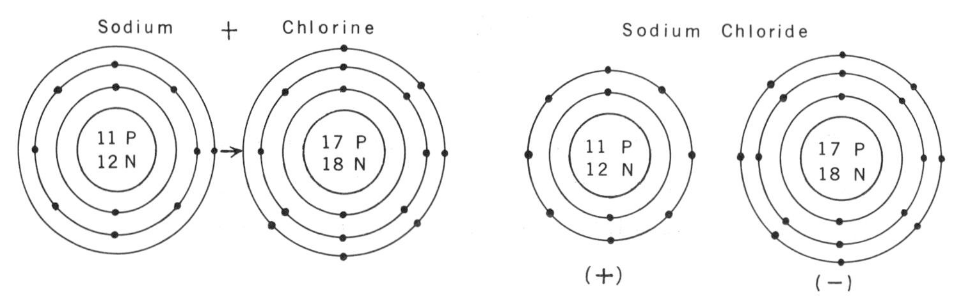

second shell of the sodium atom, and this shell is filled. So, by donating an electron, the sodium atom gains a stable outer shell. The chlorine atom also gains a stable shell, by adding the electron to the seven already present in its outer shell.

The electron transfer upsets the electrical balance, however, in the two atoms. The sodium atom, lacking one electron, now has a surplus of positive charge. Such a charged atom is called an ion. The chlorine atom, having an extra electron, becomes an ion with a surplus of negative charge. We know that opposite electrical charges attract: the two ions bearing opposite charges cling to each other. Unlike atoms linked by covalent bonds, they do not merge their electron shells, and so scientists do not usually speak of the paired atoms as a molecule.

The two atoms form the compound known as sodium chloride, common table salt. A crystal of salt is made up of millions of sodium and chlorine ions in equal numbers. When the compound dissolves in water, the ions no longer cling to each other but fall apart. Salt water thus is a solution containing free sodium and chlorine ions. When the water evaporates, however, the ions reassemble into crystal form.

Our blood is salty and so are the other fluids in the body. Free sodium and chlorine ions are an important constituent of the body.

APPENDIX B

THE STEPS IN FERMENTATION

THE FERMENTATION PROCESS begins with the glucose molecule, which is a ring compound containing a six-carbon skeleton:

```
                  CH2OH
                    |
                    C ------------------ O
              H   / |                      \        H
              |  /  H                       \       |
Glucose       C                                     C
              | \   OH                  H       /   |
             HO  \  |                   |      /    OH
                    C ------------------ C
                    |                   |
                    H                   OH
```

The first step in fermentation requires the presence of an ATP molecule. This step is promoted by an enzyme, hexokinase, which takes the outer phosphate group from the ATP molecule and attaches it to the carbon ring of the sugar. The ATP molecule is converted by this step into ADP. The sugar molecule now has a phosphate group attached and has been converted into glucose-6 phosphate. (The number refers to the particular carbon atom to which the phosphate group is attached; by custom, the carbon atoms in the ring structure are assigned numbers from 1 through 6.)

Glucose-6 Phosphate

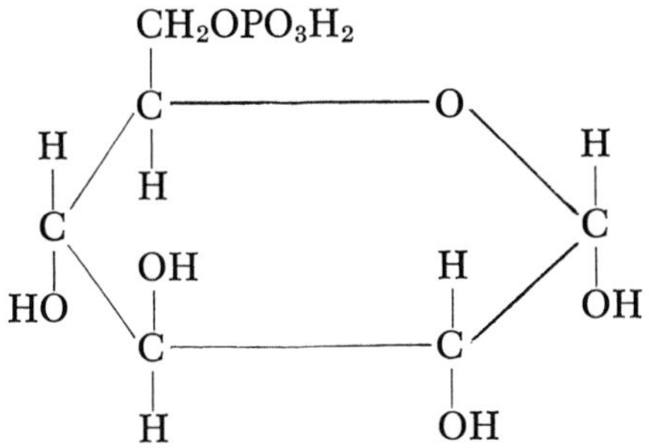

$CH_2OPO_3H_2$

Step 2 involves the enzyme phosphohexo-isomerase. This rearranges the molecule into fructofuranose-6-phosphate. At this point, the energy of another ATP molecule is required. The enzyme phosphohexo-kinase detaches a phosphate group from the ATP, converting it to ADP, and links the group to the sugar molecule. This creates fructofuranose-1,6-diphosphate.

Fructofuranose-1,6-diphosphate

$H_2O_3POH_2C$ $CH_2OPO_3H_2$

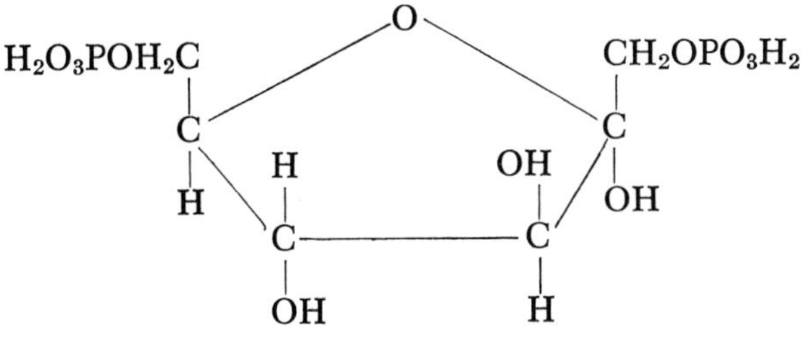

So far, no energy has been released; indeed, energy donated by two molecules of ATP has been required. However, the reaction soon will begin to yield energy as evidenced by the formation of ATP molecules. By this time, our original sugar molecule has grown a bit unwieldy with the addition of two phosphate groups. The enzyme aldose at this point splits the molecule in two halves that are very much alike. Both contain three carbon atoms and a phosphate group; they differ only in the arrangement of their atoms. One of these arrangements is called 3-phosphoglyceraldehyde and the other is named phosphodihydroxy-acetone. An enzyme, phosphotriose-isomerase, rearranges the second of these so that it also becomes 3-phosphoglyceraldehyde. So at the end of the third stage, we have two identical molecules, each with a phosphate group.

3-phosphoglyceraldehyde

```
      H                    H
      |                    |
      C=O                  C=O
      |                    |
    HCOH                 HCOH
      |                    |
      CH2OPO3H2            CH2OPO3H2
```

There are inorganic phosphate ions free in the watery medium surrounding the two molecules. Each molecule picks up one of these groups, and thus has a total of two phosphate groups. The next step involves the enzyme phosphoglyceraldehyde dehydrogenase. As its name indicates, the enzyme removes two hydrogen atoms from each molecule and transfers them to a coenzyme known as NAD, which becomes $NADH_2$. This hydrogen transfer changes each molecule into 1,3-diphosphoglyceric acid:

1,3-diphosphoglyceric Acid

$$\begin{array}{c} O \\ \| \\ C{-}O{-}PO_3H_2 \\ | \\ HCOH \\ | \\ CH_2OPO_3H_2 \end{array} \qquad \begin{array}{c} O \\ \| \\ C{-}O{-}PO_3H_2 \\ | \\ HCOH \\ | \\ CH_2OPO_3H_2 \end{array}$$

The original glucose molecule contained chemical energy stored in its bonds. By the time it has been split into two molecules of 1,3-diphosphoglyceric acid, this energy has been shifted around considerably. Each molecule of 1,3-diphosphoglyceric acid has two phosphate groups attached. Much of the stored energy is concentrated in the bond holding the group attached to the 1 carbon of the three-carbon compound. An enzyme called phosphokinase transfers the group, together with its high-energy bond, to a molecule of ADP, transforming the ADP to ATP. This process also happens to the other molecule of 1,3-diphosphoglyceric acid descended from the original glucose. So a total of two ATP molecules are formed in this step. These are now available to do various energy jobs in the cell.

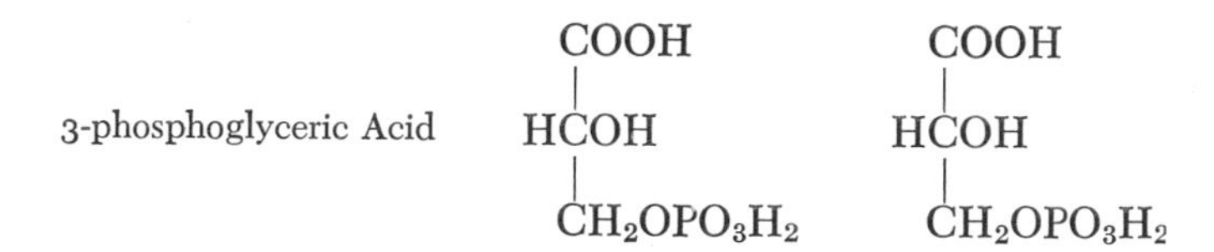

Each molecule, with its remaining phosphate group, is called 3-phosphoglyceric acid. The enzyme phosphoglyceromutase shifts the remaining phosphate group from the third to the second carbon atom in each molecule. There are then two molecules of 2-phosphoglyceric acid. From each of these, the enzyme enolase removes a molecule of H_2O water, resulting in the production of phosphoenolpyruvic acid.

$$\text{Phosphoenolpyruvic Acid} \quad \begin{array}{l} COOH \\ | \\ CO\text{—}PO_3H_2 \\ \| \\ CH_2 \end{array} \quad \begin{array}{l} COOH \\ | \\ CO\text{—}PO_3H_2 \\ \| \\ CH_2 \end{array}$$

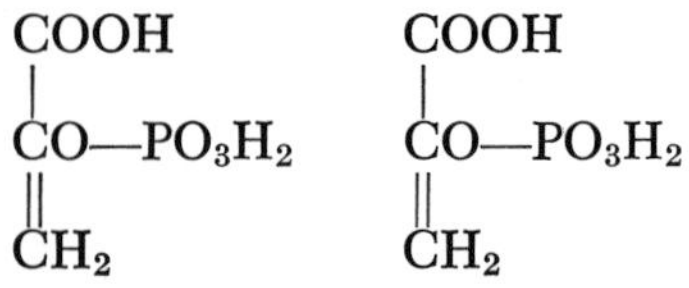

By this time, the remaining groups have acquired a large amount of energy in their bonds with their carrier molecules. The enzyme pyruvic phosphokinase transfers the phosphate groups and their bond energy to molecules of ADP, creating two molecules of ATP. This leaves the original molecules without phosphate, forming pyruvic acid.

$$\text{Pyruvic Acid} \quad \begin{array}{l} COOH \\ | \\ C{=}O \\ | \\ CH_3 \end{array} \quad \begin{array}{l} COOH \\ | \\ C{=}O \\ | \\ CH_3 \end{array}$$

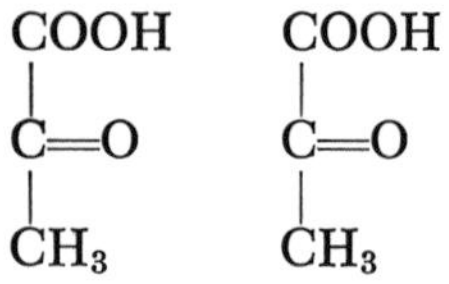

APPENDIX C

HOW DNA CONTROLS THE CELL

SCIENTISTS, IN PROBING the structure of DNA, discovered an intriguing regularity. Although DNA from different sources contained varying proportions of the four nucleotides, it was discovered that the total number of nucleotides with the base adenine always matches the total number of nucleotides with the base thymine. And for every cytosine base there is a guanine base. Another regularity emerged when X rays were used to probe the structure of the DNA molecule. It was found that the molecule has a coiled structure, something like the alpha helix of protein.

A number of researchers worked to develop schemes that might account for the known facts and, hopefully, shed light on how DNA does its job. In the spring of 1953, two scientists in Great Britain announced what they believed to be the true structure of DNA. The two men were the American James D. Watson and the Englishman Francis Crick. With Maurice Wilkins, who took some of the X-ray photographs with which they worked, they won the Nobel Prize for this feat.

The two researchers constructed a model using metal cut-outs to represent the four nucleotides. This model showed DNA as a double helix, two long molecules interwined about each other. The molecular threads were linked to each other by their bases:

```
Phosphate                 Phosphate
    +                         +
  Sugar  +  T  +  A  +  Sugar
    +                         +
Phosphate                 Phosphate
    +                         +
  Sugar  +  A  +  T  +  Sugar
    +                         +
Phosphate                 Phosphate
    +                         +
  Sugar  +  G  +  C  +  Sugar
               Etc.
```

Leaving out the phosphate and sugar groups, we can represent the DNA molecule as consisting of linked bases:

A + T
G + C
T + A
A + T
Etc.

Since an A is always linked to a T and a G to a C, the order along one side of the chain sets the order along the other side. We say that each side is "complementary" to the other. This immediately suggests how the cell is able to construct two DNA threads when it is ready to divide. The bonds between the nucleotides split. The DNA double spiral unwinds into two single chains:

A		T
G	AND	C
T		A
A		T

There is a supply of free nucleotides available in the protoplasm around the chains, and each separate chain attracts a new set of nucleotides. Every A attracts a T, and so on:

A + T		A + T
G + C	AND	G + C
T + A		T + A
A + T		A + T

The process is promoted by the enzyme DNA polymerase. Eventually, there are two complete DNA double helixes, one for each daughter cell following division. At the present time, scientists are not sure whether the chromosomes are each made up of a single DNA double helix, or a number of them hooked together in some way.

How does the DNA molecule control events in the cell outside the nucleus? Scientists knew that the DNA must exert its power through its control of enzyme construction. By directing that molecules of a certain enzyme be built, the DNA determines that a specific chemical reaction will take place. A great deal of research was required to get a clear idea of how DNA directs enzyme-building.

Scientists for quite a long time have known that DNA is not the only type of nucleic acid in the cell. There is a "cousin" nucleic acid known as RNA. RNA also is built up out of four nucleotides, three of which are adenine, cytosine, and guanine, exactly as in DNA. The fourth nucleotide in RNA, however, is uracil, as contrasted with thymine for DNA. Another difference between the two nucleic acids is that RNA usually occurs in single strands, rather than a double spiral. While almost all of the cell's DNA is found inside the nucleus, RNA is found both in the nucleus and outside it.

It has been found that protein synthesis does not take place within the nucleus but outside, in the neighborhood of small particles called ribosomes. There must be some way of sending information from the DNA to the ribosomes, and the "telegraph system" makes use of RNA. One piece of evidence that RNA has this important job is that cells that produce a great deal of protein have a correspondingly large amount of RNA in them. Also, the cell ribosomes, where protein is synthesized, are rich in RNA.

There is some RNA bound firmly to the ribosomes. It is not clear what the job is of this RNA. Other RNA molecules are found scattered through the protoplasm of the cell. These come in two varieties. One variety, distinguished by its short molecular length, is called soluble RNA. The other variety has considerably longer molecules. This variety has been found to be the RNA that carries the "message" of the DNA to the ribosomes. Thus, it is called messenger RNA.

How is the message carried? Biochemists all agree that when a protein is needed there is a section of the DNA molecule that carries the chemical information needed to create the protein. This section serves as the template, or "jig," needed for the assembly of a messenger RNA molecule. The RNA, in turn, migrates to the outer part of the cell, where, with the aid of ribosomes, it acts as the template for the formaion of a number of protein molecules (Figure C–1).

If DNA were composed of 20 different kinds of nucleotides,

C–1 A schematic representation of the steps involved in the transfer of information from DNA to the site of protein manufacture.

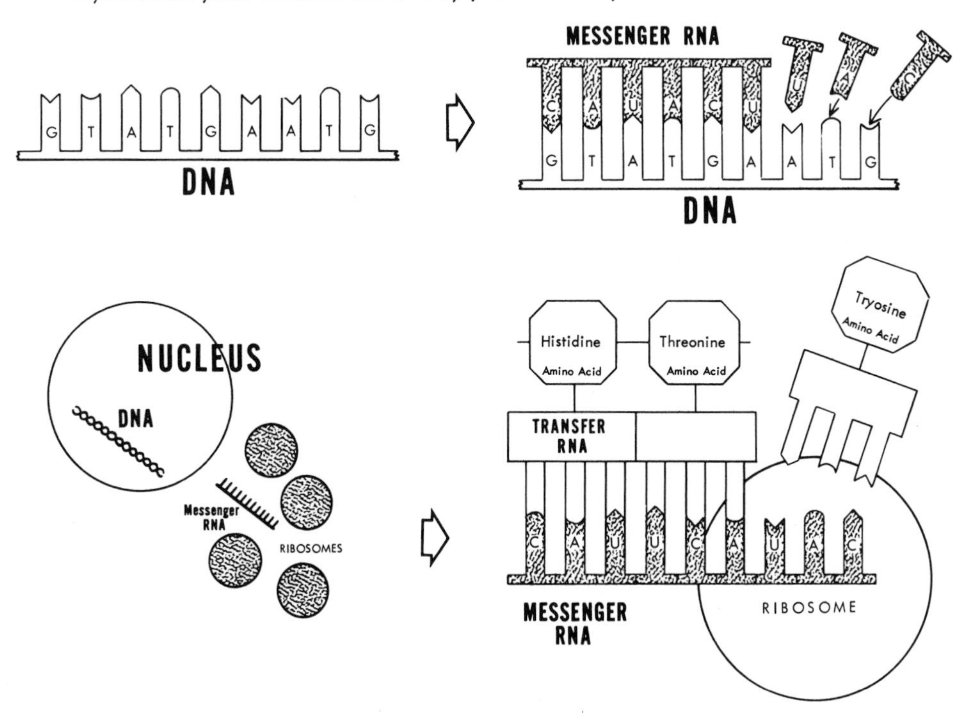

we could assume probably that each type of nucleotide represented a specific amino acid. However, with only four types of nucleotides available, this is not possible. Researchers decided that each amino acid must be represented by a certain combination of nucleotides; combinations of nucleotides would "spell out" various amino acids, just as various combinations of letters spell out different words. A number of years of painstaking research were needed before scientists were able to decipher the DNA "language," or "code." Now, however, much of this chemical language is known.

The DNA molecule, we must keep in mind, is a kind of ladder with its rungs made up of paired bases. Each DNA molecule is thousands of nucleotides long. The information for one kind of protein is carried by a section of the bases along one side of the DNA molecule.

The section of the DNA molecule that carries the information needed for one protein chain is called a "gene." When the information on the gene is needed, that section of the DNA ladder "unzips" and the paired bases come apart. The bases of the gene become exposed. Research shows that each amino acid in the protein is represented by a sequence of three bases. For example, the base sequence GTA codes for the amino acid histidine. The three-letter sequence is called a codon by scientists. The nucleotides G, A, C, and T can combine in various combinations to form more than 20 three-letter codons. Thus, there are more codons than there are amino acids. Often, two different codons will represent the same amino acid. However, each particular codon always represents the same amino acid. The "meaning" of the codon is fixed and does not change. In fact, scientists have found that the DNA language is the same in such diverse organisms as bacteria, rats, and men. They interpret this to mean that all of these organisms probably arose from a common ancestor in the distant past.

When the DNA molecule unzips to expose a gene, an enzyme attaches RNA nucleotides to the exposed segment, to form a strand of RNA (see Figure C–1). The RNA strand is complementary to the DNA; that is, the cytosine bases in the RNA are paired with the guanine bases in the DNA, RNA uracil is paired with DNA adenine, etc. If we assume that the DNA gene is made up of three codons, GTA, TGA, and ATG, then the RNA strand will carry the "words" CAU, ACU, and UAC. The strand, when completed, detaches. It drifts out of the nucleus into the cytoplasm, where it meets ribosomes. The ribosomes are the "sewing machines" that stitch amino acids together according to the instructions in messenger RNA molecules. The ribosome starts at one end of the mRNA molecule and moves along it. It "reads" the sequence of nucleotides. Meanwhile, molecules of soluble RNA are bringing amino acids to the ribosome. Because of this function, soluble RNA is often called transfer RNA, or tRNA.

There is a different kind of tRNA for each amino acid. The tRNA molecule is believed to carry an exposed sequence of three bases. If the sequence fits the code "word" on the messenger RNA, the amino acid carried by the tRNA is incorporated into the protein chain by the ribosome. The ribosome, reading the mRNA and connecting amino acids together, creates a lengthening protein chain that folds up to form the complete enzyme.

Several ribosomes can move along the messenger RNA strand simultaneously, one behind the other, each creating a protein chain. In bacteria, it is estimated that the average life span of an mRNA molecule may be two to three minutes, and the average number of protein molecules constructed from it may be in the neighborhood of 15.

When a DNA molecule unzips, what determines that an RNA strand, rather than a complementary DNA strand, is formed along the gene? It has been found that an enzyme is an important part of the process. In the presence of RNA polymerase, an RNA strand is formed along the gene. However, when the DNA strand splits in order to reproduce itself during cell division, RNA polymerase is absent. Instead, the enzyme DNA polymerase is present.

We know that the genes of the DNA molecules in the chromosomes determine what enzymes will be manufactured in the cell. These enzymes, in turn, through their role in chemical change, help determine what operations will be carried out in the cell. Now, a cell does not make use of all of its genes simultaneously. Many of them are inactive part or all of the time. One of the major problems scientists are trying to solve right now is how the cell turns genes on and off. This problem is closely related to the question of cell differentiation. In multicelled organisms, there are many specialized cells that are very different from each other, yet all contain the same DNA molecules. The difference between them is at least partly due to the fact that different types of cells use different combinations of genes. Scientists are eager to find out what causes a muscle cell, to take one example, to activitate certain genes that remain inactive in liver cells, and vice versa.

The study of viruses has helped greatly in unraveling the mysteries of the chromosomes. As mentioned earlier, a virus lacks most of the biochemical machinery possessed by cells. It is basically a "stray chromosome" equipped with a protein coat and perhaps a few enzymes that permit it to penetrate into cells. Only after entering a cell and shedding its protein coat can the virus reproduce by taking over the cell's machinery and forcing it to make new viruses.

Most viruses, like cells, carry their genetic information in the form of DNA. Once inside the cell, the DNA acts much like one of the cell's own chromosomes. It duplicates itself many times. It also forces production of certain proteins needed to form new virus coats. The DNA molecules and the proteins spontaneously aggregate together to form new viruses, which then escape from the cell. Some viruses carry their genetic information in the form of RNA, rather than DNA. Once inside the cell, the viral RNA can perform all the functions of viral DNA. It can duplicate itself, for example. However, rather than directing the manufacture of messenger RNA, the viral RNA acts as its own messenger in the manufacture of proteins.

In 1965, a team of researchers at the University of Illinois reported that by using viral RNA as a starting point, they had succeeded in duplicating that RNA in the test tube. The artificial RNA, when placed in cells, stimulated the cells to manufacture new viruses. In effect, the researchers had created active viral RNA in the test tube.

The experiment did not attract wide public attention. However, another feat in 1967 got nationwide publicity. Researchers at Stanford University in California succeeded in creating artificial viral DNA which displayed the full biological activity of the natural molecule. Because DNA is the genetic material of all cells, this synthesis was hailed as the "creation of life in a test tube."

The team included Dr. Mehran Goulian and Dr. Arthur Kornberg. Dr. Kornberg had been working with DNA for many years. It was Dr. Kornberg who discovered the enzyme DNA polymerase that promotes the construction of new DNA strands on the template of the old. Soon afterward, using a bit of natural DNA as a "primer," together with the enzyme, he was able to transform a mixture of nucleotides into artificial DNA. The artificial DNA had all the physical and chemical properties of the natural substance, but was not biologically active. In 1959, Dr. Kornberg won the Nobel Prize for this work. His research team capped the accomplishment in 1967 by creating biologically active DNA, that of the virus Phi Chi (pronounced fye kye) 174. This virus infects bacteria.

The DNA of the virus is not too complicated. It contains from five to six genes, with a total of some 5000 to 6000 codons, and 15,000 to 18,000 nucleotide "letters."

Dr. Kornberg, in commenting on the creating of the artificial virus DNA, said that he foresees the time when scientists will be able to produce active viral DNA that has been modified in certain ways. In effect, they will be producing new forms of viruses.

Although some press accounts called the experiment "creation of life in the test tube," researchers are still a very long way from actually accomplishing this feat. Most biologists would not consider any test-tube creation as "life" unless it could carry on the various functons of the complete cell, not just the DNA.

The new knowledge about DNA helps solve an old biological mystery. Men have long observed that "like gives birth to like"—in other words, offspring greatly resemble their parents and grandparents and greatgrandparents, and so on, for many generations into the past. Yet, men also have observed that, from time to time, there are small or large changes between generations. For example, a normal animal may give birth to a deformed "monster," or a plant with normally red flowers may produce a seed that grows up into a plant with white flowers. Such changes, or mutations, as they are called, are often harmful, and the offspring dies. Other changes are not harmful, and may be beneficial. In this case, the animal may survive long enough to pass on the mutation to its offspring.

Both normal inheritance and mutation can be explained on the basis of the DNA molecule. We know that the cell characteristics are mostly determined by what genes are present in the DNA. The continuity of characteristics between cell generations is guaranteed by the fact that each daughter cell gets a copy of the DNA molecules possessed by the parent cell. And, as we have seen, sexual reproduction involves the offspring's getting the pattern for half its DNA from its mother and for the other half from its father. The ability of the DNA molecule to reproduce itself accurately helps to insure that each type of plant or animal passes on its characteristics to the next generation. On the other hand, the DNA molecule is not completely immune to change. Sometimes, in duplicating itself, the molecule may make a "copying error" and the duplicate gene, for example, may have an A base where a G base was supposed to be. Or, radiation from the environment may damage a section of the DNA molecule so that it loses some "letters." Various other forms of damage can occur, too.

When this DNA damage occurs in an ordinary body cell, it is of little consequence. (Except that some damaged cells occasionally are transformed into cancerous cells that may produce harmful growths in the body.) However, suppose that a sperm cell from a male animal receives some DNA damage and then unites with an egg from a female. The offspring will have defective DNA. The defects in the DNA may be so damaging that the offspring cannot live. Or, the defects may be very small. For example, a gene may direct the manufacture of a slightly different form of enzyme than is found in other animals of the species. This enzyme may be less effective, as effective, or even better than the old form. Or, it may catalyze a new chemical reaction that leads to harmful or beneficial effects upon the organism.

Plants and animals are constantly engaged in a rather ruthless competition for the available supplies of food, water, sunlight, and other necessities. This competition tends to weed out the less fit. Mutations that enable an organism to survive longer tend to be preserved and passed on to succeeding generations. Scientists believe that the ability of DNA to both conserve and change accounts for the slow evolution of present-day plants and animals from the first cells that arose from the primeval elements of earth.

Taxonomy is the study of relationships among various plant and animal species. Among other things, the taxonomist is interested in whether certain animals, such as the tiger and the domestic cat, which share many features, are descended from a common ancestor. Taxonomy traditionally has used prominent internal and external characteristics to help classify living and fossil organism: such features as the presence of fur, the skull shape, etc. Now, the study of proteins is adding a new dimension to this field of inquiry. Biochemists have found that creatures that are closely related by evolution often have very similar proteins. For example, a certain blood protein found in man may be very much like a protein found in the blood of chimpanzees. They may have many of the same amino acids placed in much the same sequence. However, the same protein in the blood of the cat may differ quite widely in its amino acid composition and sequence. Experts in this field think that such protein clues may be an invaluable aid in resolving certain questions about evolutionary relationships.

BIBLIOGRAPHY

FOR THOSE READERS who would like to explore further the subject of life's beginnings, here are some recommended titles:

BERNAL, J. D., *The Origin of Life,* World Publishing Company, 1967, Cleveland and New York. (A discussion of the subject by one of the scientists who has contributed to it.)

BLUM, HAROLD F., *Time's Arrow and Evolution,* Princeton University Press, 1968, Princeton, N.J. (This paperback discusses some of the principles of science that are of importance in discussing the origin of life.)

FOX, SIDNEY (Editor), *The Origins of Prebiological Systems and of Their Molecular Matrices,* Academic Press, 1965, New York and London. (This book contains the scientific papers presented at the Wakulla Springs, Florida, conference in 1963 on the origin of life.)

GROBSTEIN, CLIFFORD, *The Strategy of Life,* W. H. Freeman and Company, 1965, San Francisco and London. (A paperback that attempts to give a broad perspective view of how life has arisen and evolved in the universe.)

KEOSIAN, JOHN, *The Origin of Life,* Reinhold Publishing Corporation, 1968, New York, Amsterdam, and London. (A paperback that contains considerable information about the topic.)

OPARIN, A. I., *The Chemical Origin of Life,* C. C. Thomas, 1964, Springfield, Illinois. (This book is written by one of the pioneer scientists in the field.)

Proceedings of the First International Symposium on the Origin of Life on the Earth, Pergamon Press, 1959, New York, London, Paris, and Los Angeles. (The volume contains papers presented at the Moscow scientific conference in 1957.)

RUTTEN, M. G., *The Geological Aspects of the Origin of Life on Earth,* Elsevier Publishing Company, 1962, Amsterdam and New York. (This is a very informative and well-written little book on the geology of the early Earth, and its relation to the development of life.)

INDEX